ORIGO
STEPPING STONES

2.0

COMPREHENSIVE MATHEMATICS

AUTHORS

James Burnett
Calvin Irons
Peter Stowasser
Allan Turton

PROGRAM CONSULTANTS

Diana Lambdin
Frank Lester, Jr.
Kit Norris

CONTRIBUTING WRITER

Beth Lewis

STUDENT BOOK A

ORIGO
EDUCATION

INTRODUCTION

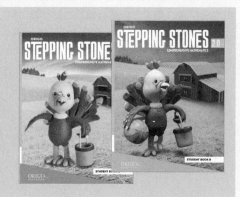

ORIGO STEPPING STONES 2.0 STUDENT JOURNAL

ORIGO Stepping Stones 2.0 is a world-class comprehensive program, developed by a team of experts to provide a balanced approach to teach and learn mathematics. The Student Journal consists of two parts — Book A and Book B. Book A comprises Modules 1 to 6, and Book B Modules 7 to 12. Each book has Lesson and Practice pages, a complete Contents, Student Glossary, and Teacher Index.

LESSON PAGES

There are two pages for each of the 12 lessons in every module. This sample shows the key components.

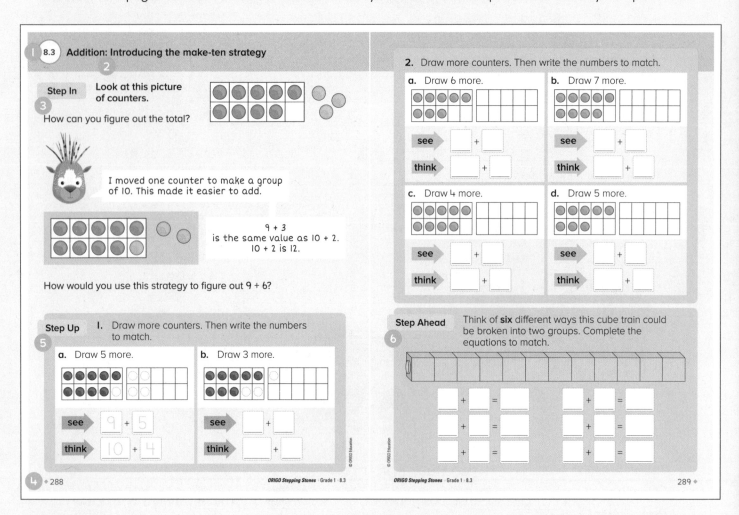

1. Module number and Lesson number.

2. The lesson title tells the content of the lesson. It has two parts: the stem (or big idea), and the leaf (which gives more details).

3. The Step In is designed to generate classroom discourse. Open questions are posed to make students think about different methods or answers.

4. For Grade 1, Book A shows a blue diamond beside each page number, and index references are in blue. Book B shows a green diamond and index references are in green.

5. Step Up provides appropriate written work for the student.

6. The Step Ahead puts a twist on each lesson to develop higher order thinking skills.

PRACTICE PAGES

Lessons 2, 4, 6, 8, 10, and 12 each provide two pages for maintaining concepts and skills. These samples show the key components.

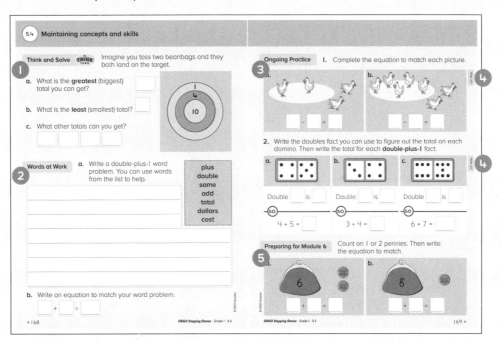

1. The *ORIGO Think Tanks* are a popular way for students to practice problem solving. There are three Think Tank problems in each module.

2. The development of written language is essential. These activities aim to help students develop their academic vocabulary, and provide opportunities for students to write their thinking.

3. Ongoing Practice revisits content previously learned. Question 1 always revisits content from a previous module, and Question 2 revisits content from the current module.

4. This tab shows the original lesson.

5. Each right-hand page provides content that prepares students for the next module.

6. Regular written practice of mental strategies is essential. There are three computation practice pages that focus on specific strategies in each module.

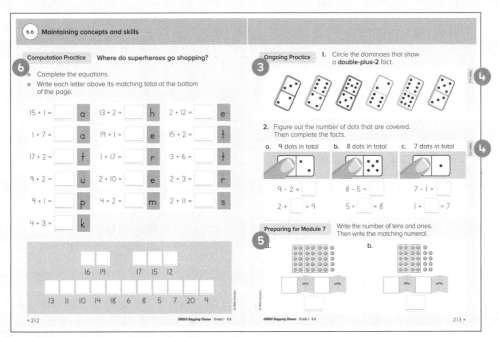

CONTENTS

© ORIGO Education

ORIGO Stepping Stones • Grade 1

CONTENTS

ORIGO Stepping Stones • Grade 1

Step In   These clowns are juggling pieces of fruit.

Count the pieces of fruit for each clown.

How many is each clown juggling?

Write each numeral in the air.

> The symbols that you write to show a number are called **numerals**.

Step Up   1.   Draw ○ to match the numeral.

a.

b.

2. Draw lines to match. There is one picture without a match.

6 ▶

2 ▶

9 ▶

5 ▶

7 ▶

Step Ahead Draw ○ on each train car to match the numeral on the side.

Step In Trace the numerals.

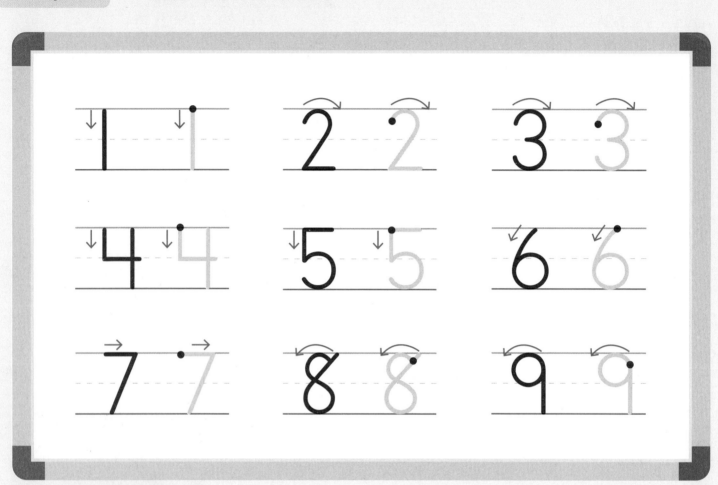

Which numerals start down ↓?

Which numerals start left ↙?

Which numerals start right ↘?

Which numerals start up ↑?

Show how you would write the numeral for zero.

Which way did you start?

     Count the fruit. Write the matching numeral.

a.

____ apples

b.

____ bananas

c.

____ oranges

d.

____ pineapples

e.
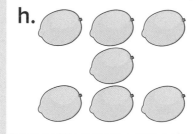
____ plums

f.

____ pear

g.

____ cherries

h.

____ lemons

i.

____ peaches

Step Ahead   Look at these telephone numbers. Circle the numerals that do not match the numerals on page 8.

| Jude | 521-6ᔕ62 | Sofia | 934-4Ɛɛ2 |
| Allison | 929-20ᐁ9 | Paul | 52ƿ-8701 |

Computation Practice ★ Write the answers as fast as you can.

start

2 + 2 = ☐

4 + 1 = ☐

5 – 2 = ☐

2 + 3 = ☐

4 – 3 = ☐

1 + 3 = ☐

1 + 1 = ☐

5 – 3 = ☐

4 – 1 = ☐

5 – 4 = ☐

4 – 2 = ☐

3 + 2 = ☐

2 – 1 = ☐

2 + 1 = ☐

5 – 5 = ☐

finish

Ongoing Practice

1. Draw a line from each coin to its name.

| penny | nickel | dime | quarter |

2. Draw lines to match.

5

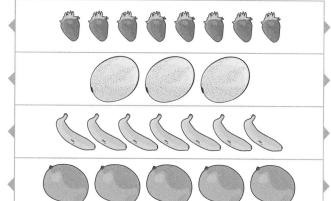

7

8

3

Preparing for Module 2

Use two colors to show two groups. Then write the number in each part and the total.

a.

[ ] add [ ] = [ ]

b.

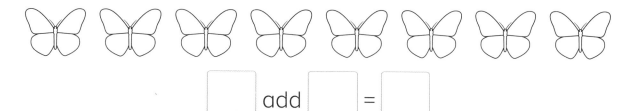

[ ] add [ ] = [ ]

Step In

How can you quickly figure out how many fingers are raised without counting each one?

I know there are 10 fingers on 2 hands. 3 fingers are down, so it is 3 less than 10.

Write the numeral to match the number of fingers that are raised.

7

Trace the number name that matches the number of fingers that are raised.

 six
 eight
 seven

Step Up

1. Write the numeral to match the number of fingers that are raised.

a.
4

b.
8

c.
6

d.
5

e.
10

f.
1

ORIGO Stepping Stones · Grade 1 · 1.3

2. Write each number name. Then draw the matching number of ◯.

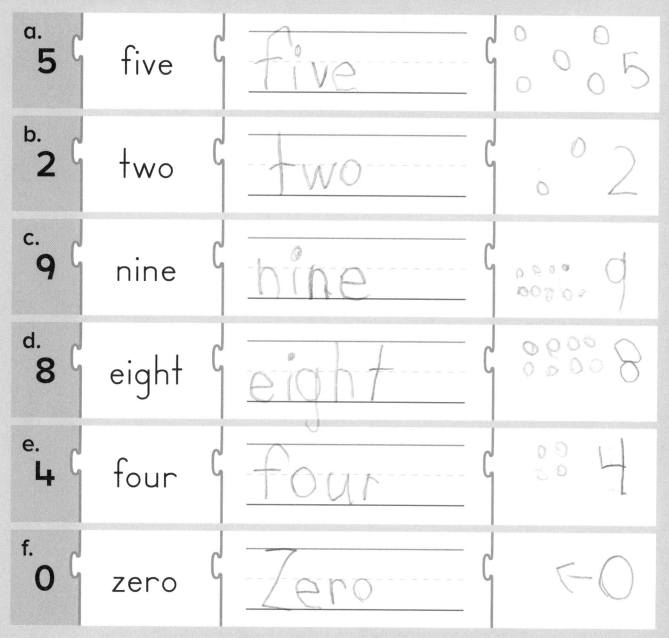

a. 5	five	five	◯ ◯ ◯ ◯ ◯ 5
b. 2	two	two	◯ ◯ 2
c. 9	nine	nine	◯◯◯◯◯ ◯◯◯◯ 9
d. 8	eight	eight	◯◯◯◯◯ ◯◯◯ 8
e. 4	four	four	◯◯ ◯◯ 4
f. 0	zero	Zero	←0

Step Ahead   Read all the clues. Then write the matching number name.

Clues

I am a three-letter word.
You say my name when
you count your eyes.
I am one less than three.

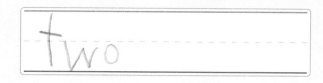
two

Step In

How many red apples do you see on the light tray?

How many green apples do you see on this tray?

11/9

15

Gavin took the green apples from the dark tray.

How many red apples do you see on this tray?

How many green apples did Gavin take?

5

Keep track of your counting by crossing out as you go.

Step Up 1. Color ◯ to match each numeral.

a. 16

b. 12

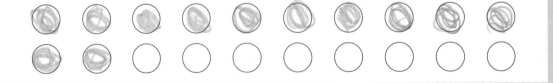

c. 19

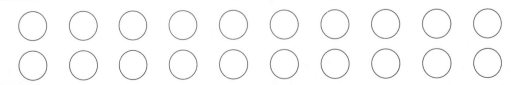

ORIGO Stepping Stones • Grade 1 • 1.4

© ORIGO Education

2. Count the fruit. Write the matching numeral.

a.
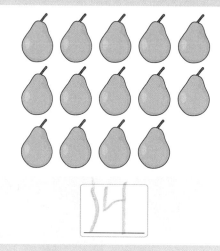

14

b.
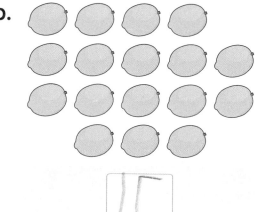

IC

c.
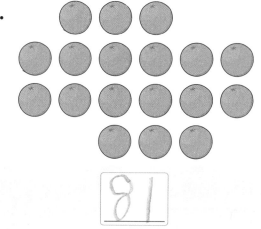

81

d.
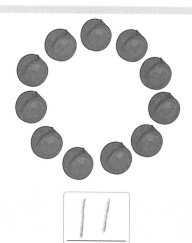

11

e.
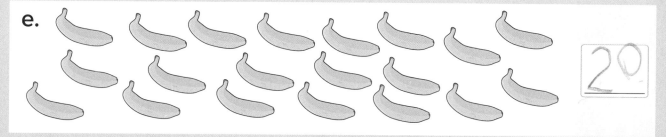

20

Step Ahead

William has 12 pennies. Draw more pennies to show a total of 12.

Think and Solve THINK TANK

a. How many dots are **inside** this shape?

b. How many dots are on the **sides** of this shape?

c. Draw a different shape that has 4 straight sides and 2 dots on the inside.

Words at Work   Choose and write a word from the list to complete each sentence below. Use each word once.

numeral

five

zero

ten

a. The number name for 5 is _____.

b. There are _____ fingers on two hands.

c. You write a _____ to show a number.

d. The number name for 0 is _____.

Ongoing Practice

I. Circle a group of coins to match the list.

I quarter

2 nickels

I dime

2. Count the fruit. Write the matching numeral.

a.

b.

c.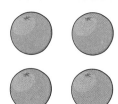

_____ apples _____ bananas _____ oranges

Preparing for Module 2

Write the numeral to match the number of dots.

a.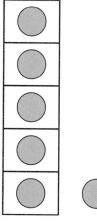

b.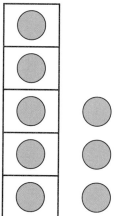

c.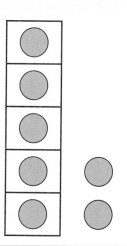

Step In

There are six counters on this ten-frame.

Draw more counters to show **sixteen**.

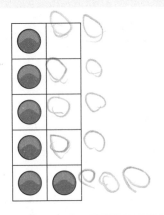

The word *teen* means *and ten*, so **sixteen** means 6 and 10.

What number does this picture show?

Trace the number name.

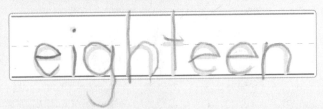
eighteen

What other teen number names could you write?

Do you think that 11 and 12 are teen numbers? What do you notice about their number names?

Step Up　1.　Write each number name.

a.	16	sixteen	Sixteen
b.	19	nineteen	nineteen
c.	14	fourteen	fourteen

ORIGO Stepping Stones · Grade 1 · 1.5

© ORIGO Education

2. Write each number name.

a.	17	seventeen	Seventeen
b.	13	thirteen	thirteen
c.	15	fifteen	fifteen
d.	11	eleven	eleven
e.	12	twelve	twelve
f.	18	eighteen	eighteen

3. Color the number names that are spelled correctly.

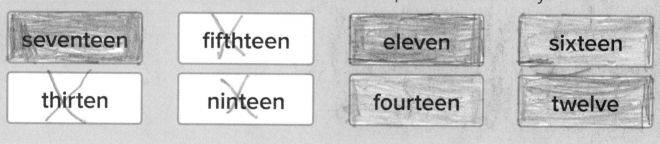

seventeen	fifthteen ✗	eleven	sixteen
thirten ✗	ninteen ✗	fourteen	twelve

Step Ahead   Kinu's brother is a teenager. Color the number names below to show what his age might be. There is more than one possible answer.

twenty	sixteen	nineteen	eight	fourteen

Step In How many  are on this ten-frame?

How do you know?

How could you use the ten-frame and extra counters to show 12, 15, or 18?

Look at the picture below.
Write the number of counters.

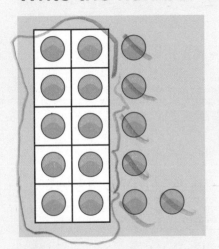

1 ten 6 ones

What do the counters beside the ten-frame show?

Step Up 1. Draw more  to match each numeral.

a.

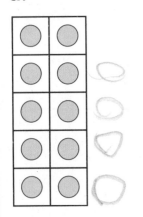

14

b.

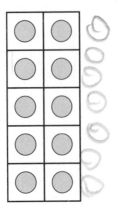

17

c.

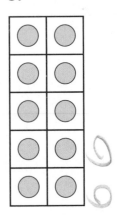

12

2. Draw ⚪ to match each numeral. Remember to fill the ten-frame first.

a.

16

b.

18

c.

11

d.

15

e.

13

f.

19

Step Ahead

This number of counters can be shown another way. Draw them using the ten-frame. Write the matching numeral.

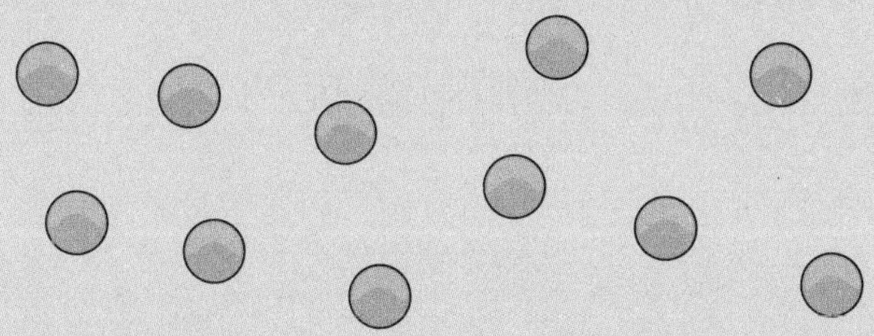

12

Computation Practice   **What kind of cup cannot hold water?**

★ Complete the equations.

★ Use a ruler to draw a straight line to join matching answers. Each line will pass through a letter.

★ Write the letter above its matching answer at the bottom of the page. Some letters are used more than once.

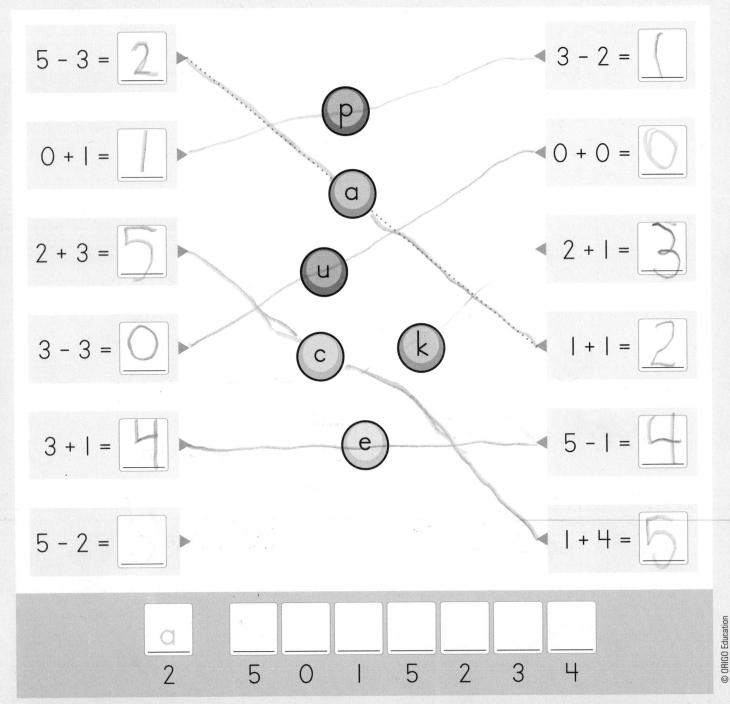

5 – 3 = 2   3 – 2 = 1

0 + 1 = 1   0 + 0 = 0

2 + 3 = 5   2 + 1 = 3

3 – 3 = 0   1 + 1 = 2

3 + 1 = 4   5 – 1 = 4

5 – 2 =   1 + 4 = 5

a							
2	5	0	1	5	2	3	4

1. Draw a line from each coin to its value.

| 1 cent | 5 cents | 25 cents | 10 cents |

2. Color ◯ to match each numeral.

a. **15**

b. **18**

c. **14**

Color the birds.
Then write a matching equation.

a. Color 3 birds red.

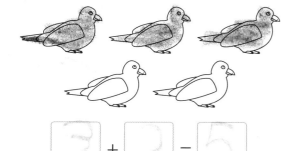

□ + □ = □

b. Color 5 birds red.

□ + □ = □

FROM K.12.3

FROM 1.1.4

Step In **Look at this picture.**

How can you figure out the number that is shown without counting all the counters?

Write the matching numeral. ____

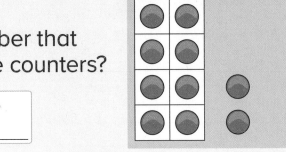

Draw ○ to show a number that is **less**.	Draw ○ to show a number that is **greater**.

Think about all the numbers that are less than 12. What different numbers could you draw?

What number is **one greater** than 12?
What number is **one less** than 12?

Step Up **1.** Write the numeral to match the number that is shown. Draw ○ to show a number that is **greater**. Then draw ○ to show a number that is **less**.

less		greater

© ORIGO Education

2. Write the numeral to match the number shown in each picture. Draw ○ to show the number that is **one greater**. Then draw ○ to show the number that is **one less**.

one less		one greater
a.		
b.		
c.		

Step Ahead — Read the problem. Then color the ○ beside the true statement.

David has 18 cards in his collection. He has one more card than Trina.

○ Trina has more cards.

○ Trina has 19 cards.

○ Trina has 17 cards.

Step In **Write the missing numbers on this number track.**

| 1 | 2 | 3 | 4 | 5 | 6 | 7 | 8 | 9 | 10 | 11 | 12 | 13 | 14 | 15 | 16 | 17 | 18 | 19 | 20 |

Use red to color the numbers that are **one greater than** and **one less than** 7. Use blue to color all the numbers that are **greater than** 15. Use green to color all the numbers that are **less than** 4.

Complete these sentences.

13 is one less than 14 .

14 is one greater than 3.

Step Up **1. Write the missing numbers. Use the number track above to help you.**

a.

| 13 | 14 | 15 |

b.

| 7 | 8 | 9 |

c.

| 9 | 10 | 11 |

d.
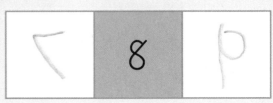

| 2 | 3 | 4 |

e.

| 8 | 9 | 10 |

f.

| 9 | 10 | 11 |

2. Write the matching number. Use the number track at the top of page 26 to help you. Some clues have more than one match.

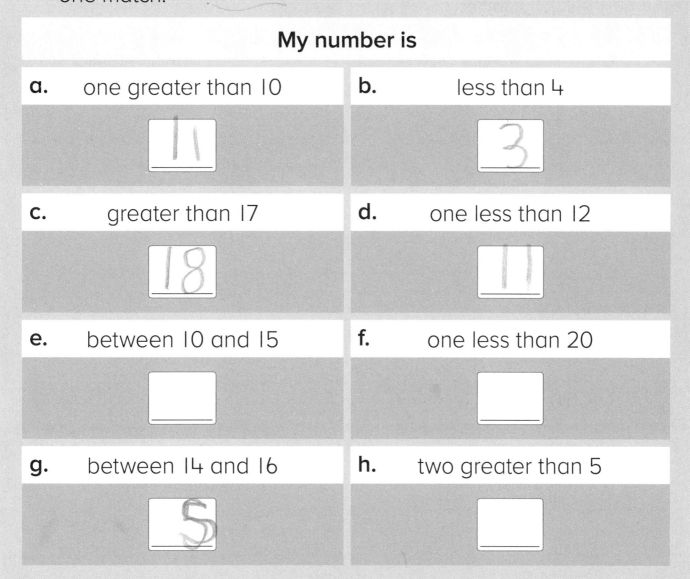

My number is

a. one greater than 10	**b.** less than 4
11	3
c. greater than 17	**d.** one less than 12
18	11
e. between 10 and 15	**f.** one less than 20
g. between 14 and 16	**h.** two greater than 5
5	

Step Ahead Three friends collect basketball cards.
Felipe has one more card than Samantha.
Jamal has one fewer card than Felipe.
How many cards could each person have?

Jamal has _____ cards.   Samantha has _____ cards.

Felipe has _____ cards.

Think and Solve Write a number to make each balance picture true.

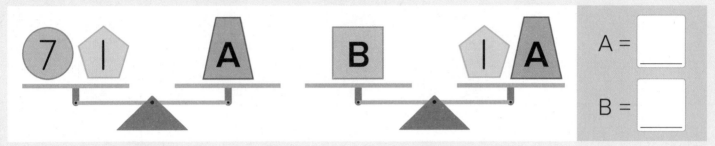

A = ____

B = ____

Words at Work

a. Choose two numbers less than 20. Write about your numbers. You can use words from the list to help you.

greater than less than	number track before	after between

b. Draw a picture to show your numbers.

Ongoing Practice

1. Color coins to show the amount on each price tag.

a.

 7 cents

b.

 15 cents

2. Draw more ○ to match each numeral.

a.
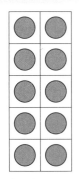

12

b.
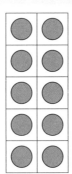

16

c.
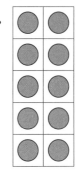

19

Preparing for Module 2

Write the amount in the purse. Write the amount being added. Then write the total.

a.

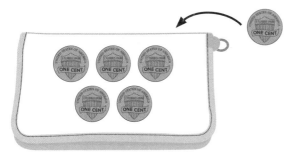

b.

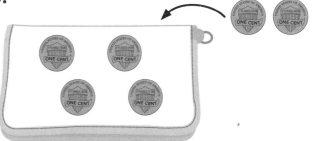 

 add equals

☐ add ☐ = ☐

Step In   What is happening in this picture?

Which athlete finished 1st?
How do you know?

Look at this toy.

Which ring went on 1st?

Which ring went on 3rd?

How could you describe the positions
of the other two rings?

Where else would you describe things as **1st**, **2nd**, and **3rd**?

Step Up   1.   Draw lines to connect the dots in order.

a.

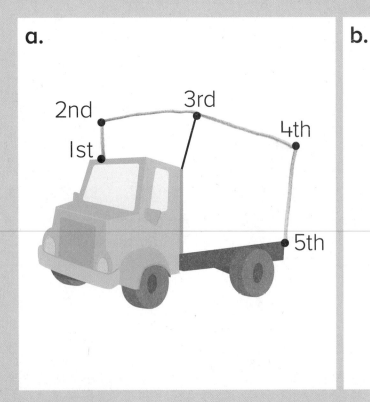

2nd   3rd
1st   4th
        5th

b.

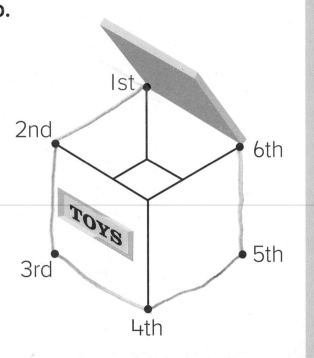

1st
2nd   6th
TOYS
3rd   5th
    4th

2. Draw ⌢ to connect the dots in order.

a.

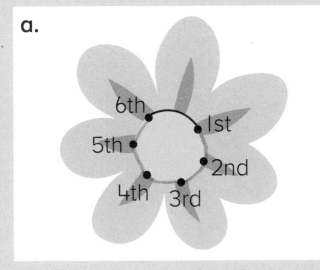

6th 1st
5th 2nd
4th 3rd

b.

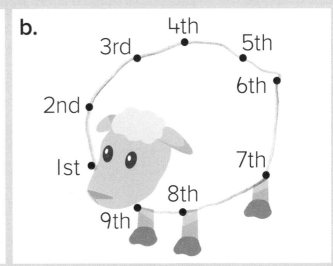

4th
3rd 5th
2nd 6th
1st 7th
8th
9th

3. The 1st scoop of frozen yogurt is strawberry.
Color these scoops.

a. Color the 2nd scoop blue.

b. Color the 4th scoop red.

c. Color the 3rd scoop green.

Step Ahead

Draw 😊 in the **1st**, **3rd**, **5th**, **7th**, and **9th** positions.
Then draw ☹ in the other positions to make a pattern.

 start here

Write the name of the last position. 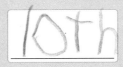 10th

Step In Describe the order of the cars in this race.

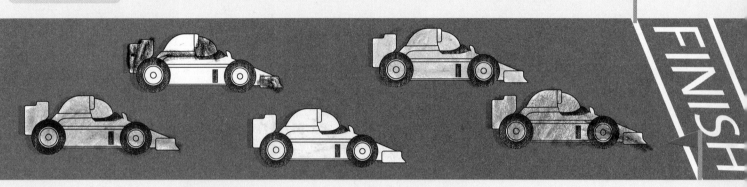

Use green to color the car that will finish 2nd.
Use blue to color the car that will finish last.

Use yellow to color the car that will finish 3rd.
Use red to color the car that will finish first.

In which position will the other car finish? How do you know?

Step Up 1. Draw lines to connect cars and their ribbons.

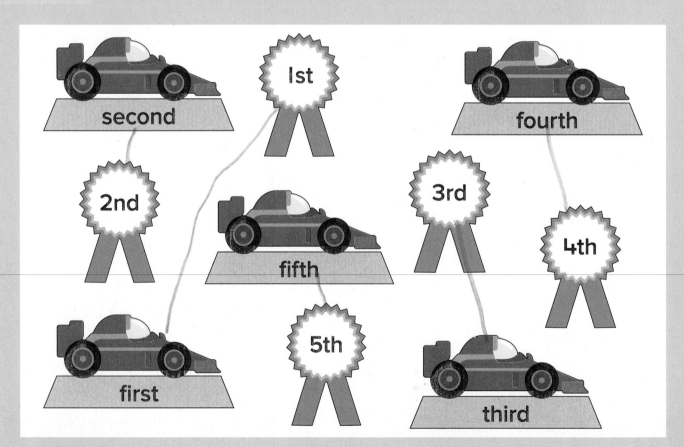

© ORIGO Education

2. The first plane is shaded. Color other planes to match the instructions.

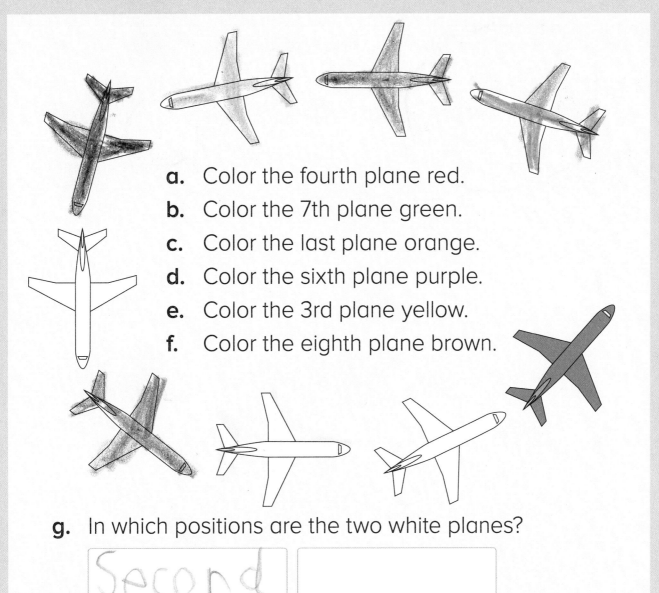

a. Color the fourth plane red.

b. Color the 7th plane green.

c. Color the last plane orange.

d. Color the sixth plane purple.

e. Color the 3rd plane yellow.

f. Color the eighth plane brown.

g. In which positions are the two white planes?

Second [ ]

Step Ahead In each race, Australia finished two places after the USA. Write the missing positions for each race.

Australia	USA		Australia	USA		Australia	USA
6th	___		___	1st		4th	___

Australia	USA		Australia	USA		Australia	USA
___	3rd		10th	___		___	7th

© ORIGO Education

Computation Practice

Tuesday and Thursday start with the letter T. What other two days start with T?

★ Complete the equations.

★ Write the letter in each box above its matching answer at the bottom of the page.

$4 - 2 = \boxed{2}$ **d**

$1 - 1 = \boxed{0}$ **r**

$2 + 1 = \boxed{3}$ **n**

$5 - 1 = \boxed{4}$ **t**

$3 + 2 = \boxed{}$ **o**

$4 - 3 = \boxed{}$ **y**

Some letters are used more than once.

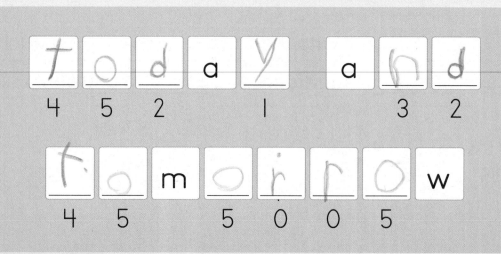

t	o	d	a	y		a	n	d
4	5	2		1			3	2

t	o	m	o	r	r	o	w
4	5		5	0	0	5	

I. Keep the patterns going.

a.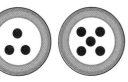

FROM K 12.5

b. ○△○○△○○△○

2. Write the numeral to match the number shown. Draw ○ to show the number that is **one greater**. Then draw ○ to show the number that is **one less**.

FROM 1.1.7

one less		one greater

Preparing for Module 2

Complete the equation. Write the **greater** number first.

a.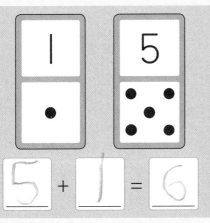

$5 + 1 = 6$

b.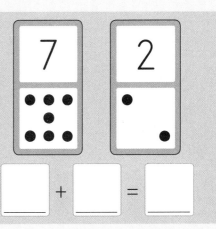

$\square + \square = \square$

Step In

In this graph, one face means one vote.

What does the graph tell you? 64

How many students have been to a farm?

How many students have not been to a farm?

How many students voted in total?

Complete this equation to show how many more students have been to a farm than those who have not been to a farm.

Have you been to a farm?

Yes   No

Step Up

1. Read this question to some other students. Draw a 😊 in the graph to show each answer.

Do you like jigsaw puzzles?						
Yes	😊	😊	😊	😊	😊	😊
No						

2. Look at the graph in Question I to answer each question.

a.

How many students like jigsaw puzzles?

b.

How many students do not like jigsaw puzzles?

c.

How many students voted in total?

d.

Is the number of students who like jigsaw puzzles greater than the number of students who do not like jigsaw puzzles?

Step Ahead

Draw ☺ in the graph to match each clue.

Clue I
Three students voted No.

Clue 2
More students voted Yes than No.

Clue 3
Eight students voted in total.

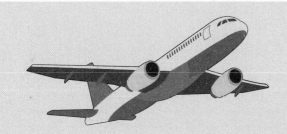

Have you ever been to another country?

Yes   No

Step In

A group of students voted for their favorite animal at the zoo. They each placed a counter beside their favorite animal to show their vote.

Our Favorite Animal at the Zoo

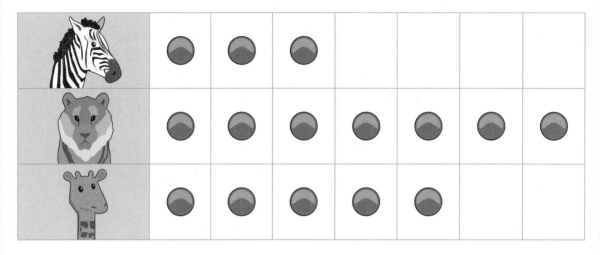

What does the graph tell you?
What is the most popular animal at the zoo?

How many students voted for each animal?
How many students voted in total?

How many more students voted for the tiger than the **giraffe**?

Step Up

1. Ask the students in your class to vote for their favorite animal. Draw a ✔ to show each vote.

2. Draw ⬤ beside the animals to show each vote from Question 1.

3. Look at the graph above to answer each question.

a. How many students voted for the giraffe? ⬜

b. How many students voted in total? ⬜

c. Which animal is the most popular? ⬜

d. Is the number of students who voted for the giraffe greater than the number of students who voted for the zebra? ⬜

e. Is the number of students who voted for the tiger greater than the number of students who voted for the giraffe? ⬜

Step Ahead

Look at the graph at the top of page 38. Can you tell the animal that is most popular without counting the number of counters beside each animal? Share your thinking with another student.

Think and Solve

What number am I? __6__

- I am less than 12.
- I am greater than 4 + 5.
- I am not 10.

Words at Work

Write the answer for each clue in the grid.
Use words from the list.

Clues Across

1. 14 has one __ and 4 ones.
4. 15 is __ than 12.
5. A graph is used to show __.
6. 13 is __ than 16.

Clues Down

2. 18 is the __ that matches eighteen.
3. 10 is __ 9 and 11.

numeral
ten
data
between
greater
less

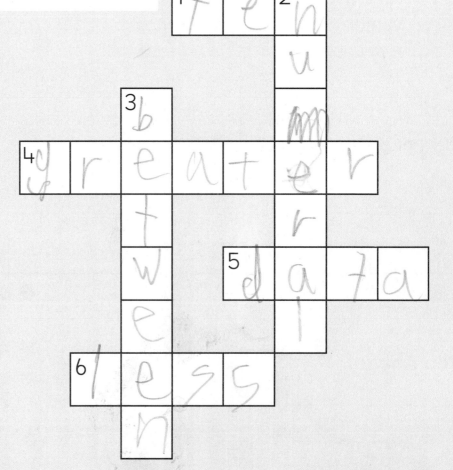

Ongoing Practice

1. Look at the pattern. Draw the missing parts.

2. Draw lines to connect the dots in order.

a.

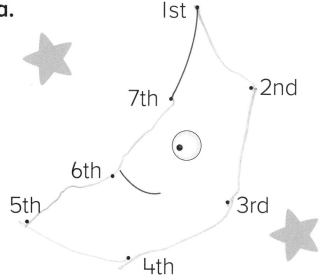

1st
2nd
7th
6th
5th
4th
3rd

b.

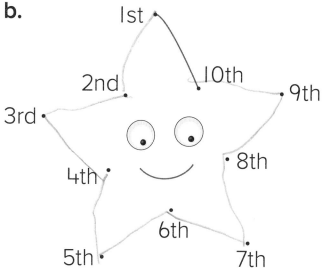

1st
2nd 10th 9th
3rd
4th 8th
5th 6th 7th

Preparing for Module 2   Write two equations to match each domino.

a.

3 + 5 = 8

5 + 3 = 8

b.

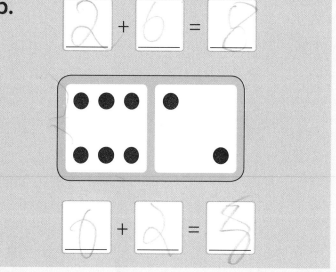

2 + 6 = 8

6 + 2 = 8

Step In   What is happening in this picture?

How many bears are on the bus?
How many bears are getting on the bus?
What is the total number of bears?

Write the equation to match.

$$4 + 2 = 6$$

How many blue backpacks can you see?
How many white backpacks can you see?
What is the total number of backpacks?

Write the equation to match.

$$3 + 1 = 4$$

What equation would show the total number of bears wearing hats?

Step Up   1.   Solve each problem. Write the equation to match.

a. 4 bears are on a bus. 3 more bears get on. How many bears are now on the bus?

$$4 + 3 = 7$$

b. One bear is on a bus. 4 more bears get on. How many bears are on the bus?

$$1 + 4 = 5$$

2. Color the bears. Then write an equation to match.

a. Color 5 bears brown.

$$5 + 2 = 7$$

b. Color 2 bears brown.

$$2 + 5 = 7$$

c. Color 4 bears brown.

$$4 + 4 = 8$$

d. Color 3 bears brown.

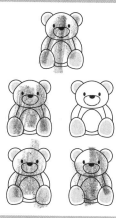

$$3 + 2 = 5$$

Step Ahead Use counters to help solve this problem.

5 bears are sitting on the bus.
One bear gets off the bus.
Then 3 more bears get on the bus.
How many bears are now on the bus?

☐ bears

Step In

What is a quick way to figure out the total number of fingers raised?

I see 5 and 2.
5 is bigger,
so I can count
on from 5.
That is 5...6...7.

5

Use your quick way to figure out the total number of cubes.

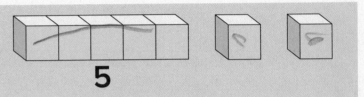

5

Step Up

1. Start at 5 and count on. Write the numbers **you say**.

a.

| 5 | 6 | 7 | 8 |

b.

| 5 | 6 |

c.

| 5 | 6 | 7 |

2. Start at 5 and count on. Write the total.

a.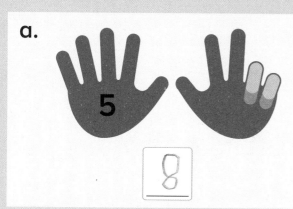

8

b.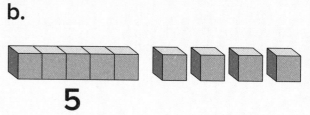

5

9

c.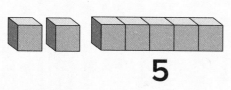

5

7

d.

5

6

e.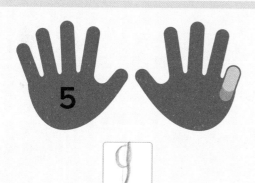

5

9

f.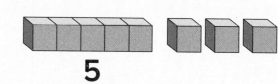

5

8

Step Ahead Write an addition equation to match each picture.

a.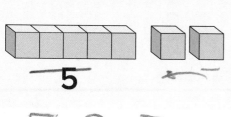

5

5 + 5 = 7

b.

5

Computation Practice

★ Complete the equations.

★ Write the letter in each box above its matching answer at the bottom of the page.

$3 + 1 = 4$ n

$3 - 3 = 0$ v

$2 - 1 = 1$ s

$5 - 3 = 2$ a

$4 - 1 = 3$ e

$5 + 0 = 5$ p

Some letters are used more than once.

a	n	t	s
2	4		1

n	e	v	e	r
4	3	0	3	

s	l	e	e	p
1		3	3	5

Ongoing Practice

1. Write the matching numeral beside each picture. Then draw a line from each picture to its matching number name.

7 ___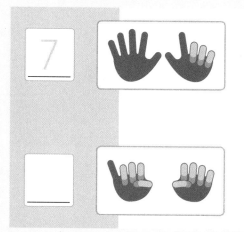

___

ten

one

three

seven

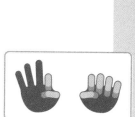 ___

 ___

2. Color the mice. Then write an equation to match.

a. Color 2 mice brown.

☐ + ☐ = ☐

b. Color 3 mice brown.

☐ + ☐ = ☐

Preparing for Module 3

Write the numeral to match the number of counters.

a.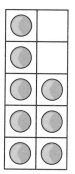

☐

b.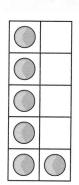

☐

c.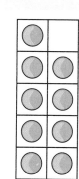

☐

d.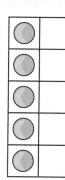

☐

Step In

What is the easiest way to figure out the total number of dots on this card?

What addition fact could you write?

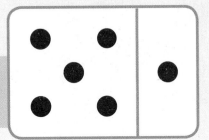

$$5 + 1 = 6$$

What are some other facts you could figure out this way?

Step Up

1. Count on 1, 2, or 3 to figure out the total. Then write the addition fact.

a.

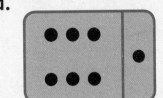

$$6 + 1 = 5$$

b.

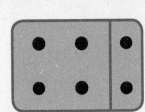

$$4 + 2 = 6$$

c.

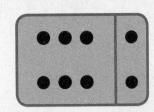

$$6 + 2 = 8$$

d.

$$3 + 1 = 4$$

e.

$$5 + 3 = 8$$

f.

$$3 + 2 = 5$$

2. Write the addition fact to match each card.

a.

$\boxed{5} + \boxed{2} = \boxed{7}$

b.

$\boxed{8} + \boxed{1} = \boxed{7}$

c.

$\boxed{9} + \boxed{3} = \boxed{12}$

d.

$\boxed{6} + \boxed{3} = \boxed{9}$

e.

$\boxed{8} + \boxed{0} = \boxed{8}$

f.

$\boxed{} + \boxed{} = \boxed{}$

3. Count on 1 or 2 to figure out the total.
Then write the addition fact.

a.
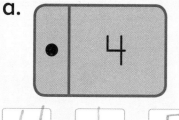
$\boxed{4} + \boxed{1} = \boxed{5}$

b.

$\boxed{7} + \boxed{1} = \boxed{8}$

c.

$\boxed{8} + \boxed{2} = \boxed{10}$

Step Ahead   Look at the total. Draw the missing dots on the card.
Then complete the addition fact.

a.
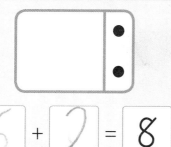
$\boxed{6} + \boxed{2} = \boxed{8}$

b.
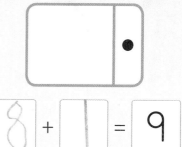
$\boxed{8} + \boxed{1} = \boxed{9}$

Step In

There are **6** pennies in this purse and some outside the purse.

How could you figure out the total number of pennies?

What addition fact could you write?

$$4 + 2 = 6$$

Step Up

1. Count on 1 or 2 pennies.
Then write the addition fact.

a.

$$4 + 2 = 6$$

b.

$$6 + 1 = 4$$

c.

$$5 + 1 = 6$$

d.

$$7 + 2 = 9$$

© ORIGO Education

2. Write an equation to solve each problem.

a. 5 books are on a desk. 2 more books are put on the desk. How many are on the desk now?

5   o o

$5 + C = \Gamma$

b. 4 friends are swimming. One more friend jumps in. How many friends are swimming now?

4   o

$4 + 1 = 5$

c. There are 6 toys on a table and 3 toys on the floor. How many toys are there in total?

6   o o o o

$6 + 3 = 9$

d. 9 birds are sitting in a tree. 2 more birds fly to the tree. How many birds are sitting in the tree now?

9   o o

$9 + 2 = 11$

3. Write the totals.

a. $3 + 2 = 5$

b. $7 + 1 = 8$

c. $8 + 2 = 10$

d. $9 + 0 = 9$

e. $4 + 3 = \Gamma$

f. $3 + 1 = 4$

Step Ahead

There are 13 pennies in total. How many are in the purse?

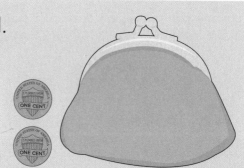

_____ pennies

Think and Solve Write a number to make each balance picture true.

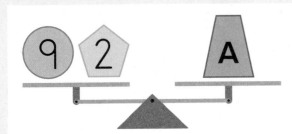 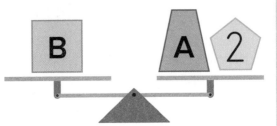

A = _____

B = _____

Words at Work

a. Write an addition story. You can use words from the list to help you.

| add |
| equals |
| makes |
| join |
| and |
| total |
| group |

b. Draw a picture to match your story.

c. Write an equation to match. _____ + _____ = _____

© ORIGO Education

Ongoing Practice

1. Write the numeral to match each picture.

a.

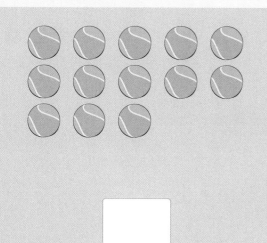

b.

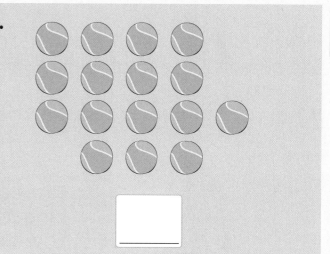

2. Write the addition fact to match each card.

a.

$\boxed{} + \boxed{} = \boxed{}$

b.

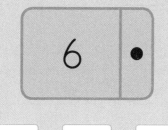

$\boxed{} + \boxed{} = \boxed{}$

c.

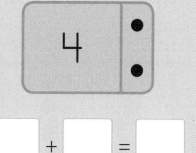

$\boxed{} + \boxed{} = \boxed{}$

Preparing for Module 3   Write the number of tens and ones.

a.

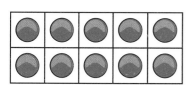

$\boxed{}$ ten and $\boxed{}$ ones

b.

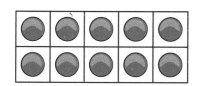

$\boxed{}$ ten and $\boxed{}$ ones

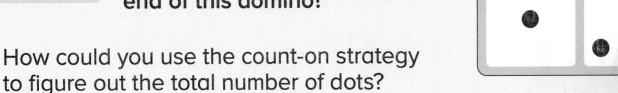

Step In

How many dots are on each end of this domino?

How could you use the count-on strategy to figure out the total number of dots?

What number would you start with?

It's easier to start with the **bigger** number, and count on the **smaller** number.

In what order would you add the dots on these dominoes?

Step Up

1. Write the numeral to show each number of dots. Then circle the number that is **greater**.

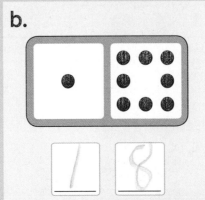

a.   2   5

b.   1   8

c.   ☐   ☐

2. Start with the **greater** number. Count on the **smaller** number. Then write the total.

a.

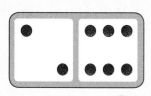

6 + 2 = 8

b.

5 + 3 = 8

c.

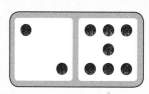

7 + 2 = 9

d.

4 + 3 = 7

e.

8 + 2 = 11

f.

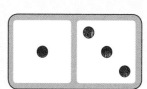

3 + 1 = 4

3. Figure out the total number of dots. Write an equation to show the best order to add the dots.

a.

1 + 4 = 5

b.

6 + 3 = 9

c.

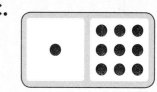

10 + 1 = 11

Step Ahead   Circle the number that you say first to figure out the total. Then complete the equation.

a. 2 + 4 = 6

b. 7 + 1 = 8

c. 3 + 8 = 11

d. 5 + 1 = 6

e. 6 + 1 = 7

f. 0 + 9 = 9

Step In   **What do you notice about these pictures?**

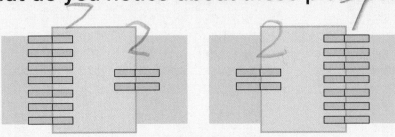

What addition fact would match each picture?

These facts are called turnaround facts.

What number will you say first?
What number will you count on?

Step Up   I. Complete the addition fact and its turnaround fact.

a.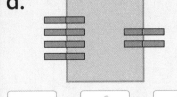

$4 + 2 = 6$
$2 + 4 = 6$

b.

$1 + 6 = 7$
$6 + 1 = 7$

c.

$6 + 2 = 8$
$2 + 6 = 8$

d.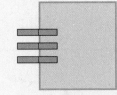

$2 + 5 = 7$
$5 + 2 = 7$

e.

$3 + 0 = 3$
$0 + 3 = 3$

f.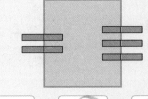

$2 + 3 = 5$
$3 + 2 = 5$

ORIGO Stepping Stones · Grade 1 · 2.6

© ORIGO Education

2. Write the addition fact. Then write the turnaround fact.

a.

$1 + 7 = 8$

$7 + 1 = 8$

b.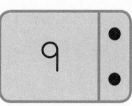

$9 + 2 = 11$

$2 + 9 = 11$

c.

$3 + 5 = 8$

$5 + 3 = 8$

d.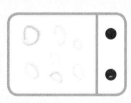

$8 + 1 = 9$

$1 + 8 = 9$

e.

$0 + 6 = 6$

$6 + 0 = 6$

f.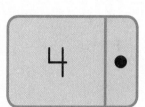

$4 + 1 = 5$

$1 + 4 = 5$

Step Ahead Look at the total. Draw the missing dots on the card. Then write two addition facts to match.

a.

$\boxed{} + \boxed{} = 10$

$\boxed{} + \boxed{} = \boxed{}$

b.

$\boxed{} + \boxed{} = 11$

$\boxed{} + \boxed{} = \boxed{}$

Computation Practice

★ Complete the equations.

★ Draw a line from each ball to the flag that matches.

★ Circle the ball that has no match.

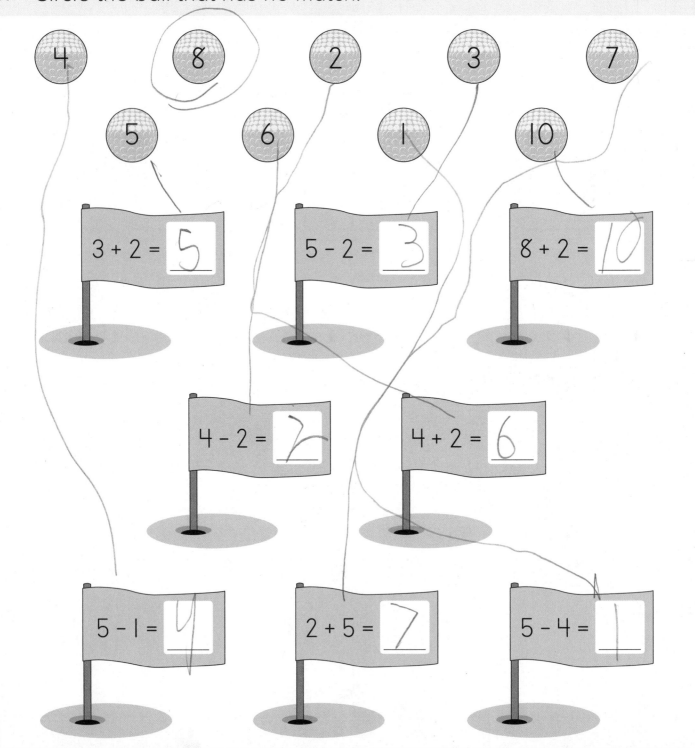

$3 + 2 = 5$

$5 - 2 = 3$

$8 + 2 = 10$

$4 - 2 = 2$

$4 + 2 = 6$

$5 - 1 = 4$

$2 + 5 = 7$

$5 - 4 = 1$

1. Draw ◯ to match each numeral. Remember to fill the ten-frame first.

a.

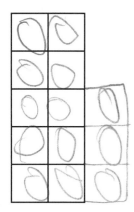

13

b.

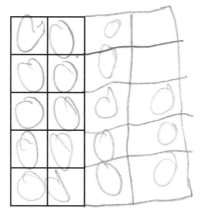

18

c.

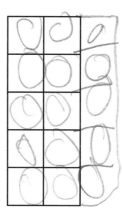

15

2. Start with the **greater** number. Count on the **smaller** number. Then write the total.

a.

7 + 3 = 10

b.

5 + 2 = 7

c.

6 + 1 = 7

Preparing for Module 3

Write the number name to match each numeral.

a.
6

six   Six   Six

b.
8

eight

FROM 1.1.6

FROM 1.2.5

© ORIGO Education

Step In   What is happening in this picture?

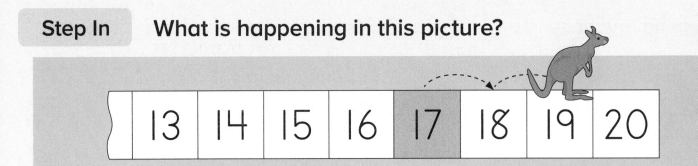

Which number did the kangaroo start on?

Which number did the kangaroo finish on?
How many jumps did it make?

What addition equation would you write
to match this picture?

What turnaround equation would you write?

$$17 + 2 = 19$$

$$2 + 17 = 19$$

Step Up   1. Count on 1 or 2. Write an addition equation to match.
Then write the turnaround equation.

a.

| 11 | 12 | 13 | 14 | 15 | 16 | 17 | 18 | 19 | 20 |

$$12 + 2 = 14$$

$$2 + 12 = 14$$

b.

| 11 | 12 | 13 | 14 | 15 | 16 | 17 | 18 | 19 | 20 |

$$16 + 2 = 18$$

$$2 + 16 = 18$$

c.

| 11 | 12 | 13 | 14 | 15 | 16 | 17 | 18 | 19 | 20 |

$$18 + 1 = 19$$

$$1 + 18 = 19$$

2. Draw jumps to help you count on. Then write the matching addition equation and the turnaround equation.

a. Count on **2**.

| 11 | 12 | 13 | 14 | 15 | 16 | 17 | 18 | 19 | 20 |

$11 + 2 = 13$

$2 + 11 = 13$

b. Count on **1**.

| 11 | 12 | 13 | 14 | 15 | 16 | 17 | 18 | 19 | 20 |

$13 + 1 = 14$

$1 + 13 = 14$

c. Count on **2**.

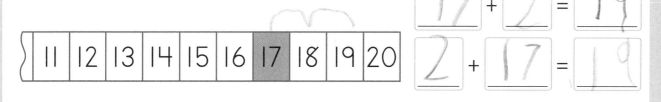

| 11 | 12 | 13 | 14 | 15 | 16 | 17 | 18 | 19 | 20 |

$17 + 2 = 19$

$2 + 17 = 19$

d. Count on **1**.

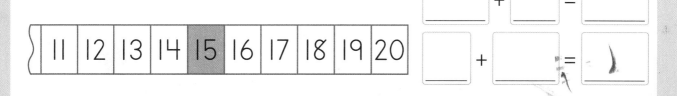

| 11 | 12 | 13 | 14 | 15 | 16 | 17 | 18 | 19 | 20 |

$\_\_ + \_\_ = \_\_$

$\_\_ + \_\_ = \_\_$

Step Ahead   Draw jumps to match each equation.

| 1 | 2 | 3 | 4 | 5 | 6 | 7 | 8 | 9 | 10 | 11 | 12 | 13 | 14 | 15 |

$3 + 1 = 4$ $12 + 2 = 14$

Step In

One hand shows one group of five fingers.

When you double five, you get two groups of five.

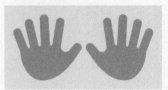

What addition fact would you write to show the total number of fingers?

$5 + 5 = 10$

What doubles do these pictures show?

What other doubles have you seen?

Step Up

1. Write numbers to match the double.

a.

$3 + 3 = 6$

double $3 = 6$

b.

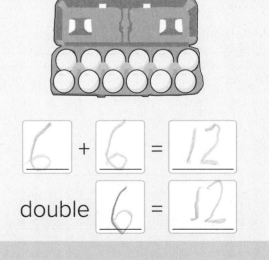

$6 + 6 = 12$

double $6 = 12$

2. Draw the same number of dots on the other wing.
Then write the numbers.

a.

4 + 4 = 8

double 4 = 8

b.

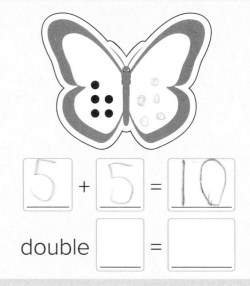

5 + 5 = 10

double ___ = ___

c.

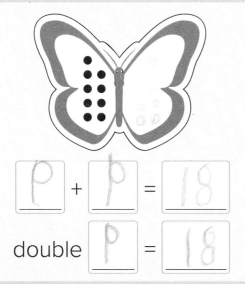

9 + 9 = 18

double 9 = 18

d.

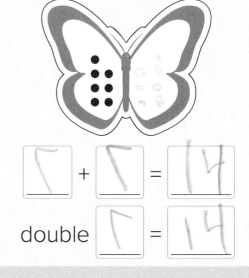

7 + 7 = 14

double 7 = 14

Step Ahead

Draw dots to show
double 8. Then write the
matching facts below.

4 + 4 = 8

double 4 = 8

Think and Solve Imagine this pattern keeps going.

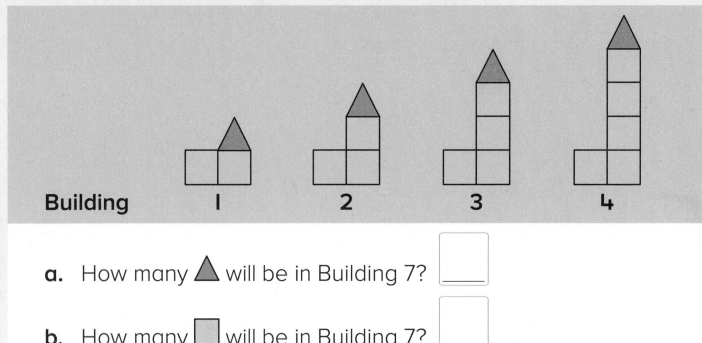

Building   1   2   3   4

a. How many ▲ will be in Building 7? ☐

b. How many ◻ will be in Building 7? ☐

c. How many shapes will be in Building 10 in total? ☐

Words at Work   Write about **adding 5 and 2**. You can use words from the list to help you.

| add |
| equals |
| makes |
| balances |
| and |
| count on |
| total |

Ongoing Practice

1. Circle the object that has been sorted into the wrong group.

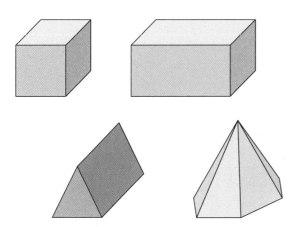
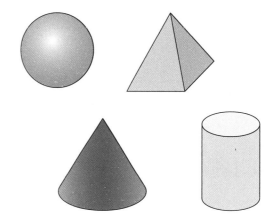

2. Count on 1 or 2. Then write the matching addition fact and the turnaround fact.

Preparing for Module 3

Draw ◯ to match each numeral. Remember to fill the ten-frame first.

a.

b.

c.

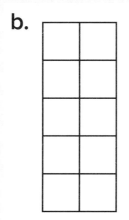

15

19

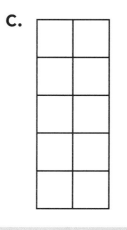

12

Step In Beads are threaded onto two pieces of string.

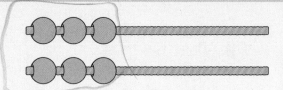

Complete the doubles fact to match the picture. Then draw more beads to show double 5.

$3 + 3 = 6$

What doubles fact does this picture show?
How could you figure out the total?

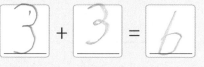

I don't know double 8, but I know that double 5 is 10, and that double 3 is 6.

Double 5 is 10

Double 3 is 6

SO

Double 8 is 16

What is another double you could figure out the same way?

Step Up I. Use the same strategy to figure out these.

a.
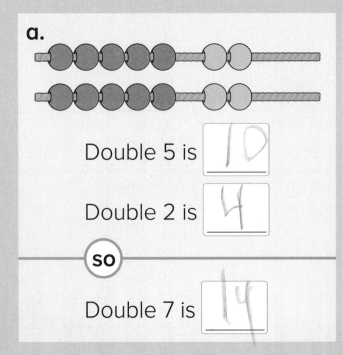

Double 5 is 10

Double 2 is 4

SO

Double 7 is 14

b.
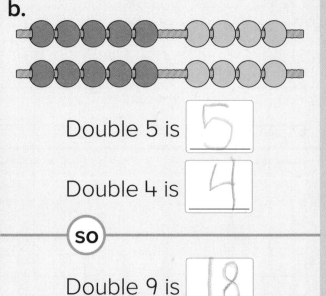

Double 5 is 5

Double 4 is 4

SO

Double 9 is 18

2. Write the doubles fact to match each domino.

a.

$4 + 4 = 8$

b.

$6 + 6 = 12$

c.

$5 + 5 = 10$

d.

$8 + 8 = 16$

e.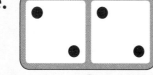

$2 + 2 = 4$

f.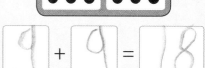

$9 + 9 = 18$

3. Complete each doubles fact.
Draw dots on the domino to help your thinking.

a. Double **8**

$8 + 8 = 16$

b. Double **6**

$6 + 6 = 12$

c. Double **7**

$7 + 7 = 12$

Step Ahead Write the doubles fact to match each total.

a. $5 + 5 = 10$

b. $18 = 9 + 9$

c. $8 + 8 = 16$

d. $4 = 2 + 2$

e. $1 + 1 = 2$

f. $12 = 6 + 6$

Step In   This type of clock is called an analog clock.
Where might you see an analog clock?

What numbers do you see on this clock?
What do you think the numbers are counting?

Which hand is the **hour hand**?

The short hand is the hour hand.
It shows the name of the hour
and counts the hours.

The long hand is called the **minute hand** because it counts the minutes.

When the minute hand is pointing to 12 it is the **start** of another hour.

This time is **on the hour** and it is an **o'clock** time.

What time is the clock showing? How do you know?

Step Up   **I.** Write each time.

a.

___8___ o'clock

b.

___3___ o'clock

c.

___10___ o'clock

ORIGO Stepping Stones · Grade 1 · 2.10

2. The **minute** hand is the **long** hand. Draw the minute hand on each clock to show an hour time. Then write the time.

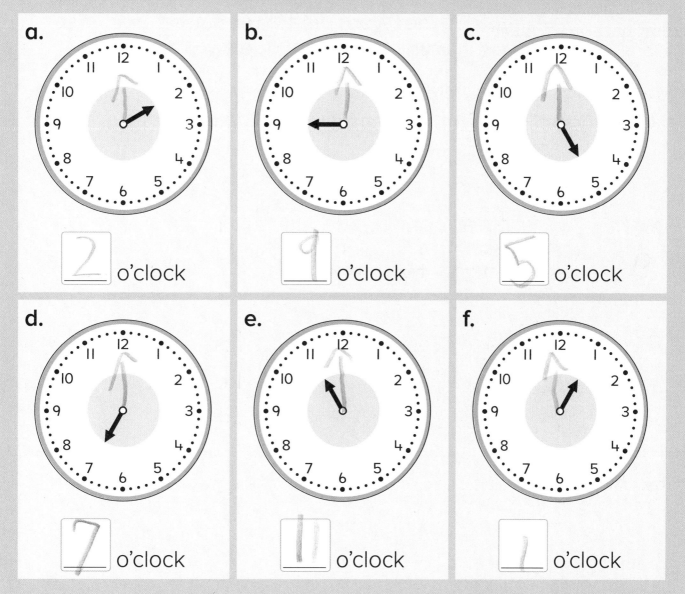

a.

2 o'clock

b.

9 o'clock

c.

5 o'clock

d.

7 o'clock

e.

11 o'clock

f.

1 o'clock

Step Ahead   Circle the clocks that show a time on the hour.

Computation Practice

What word with three letters becomes fewer when you add two more?

★ Complete the equations.
★ Color each total in the puzzle below.

Some totals appear more than once.

$2 + 4 = 6 = 4 + 2$

$1 + 2 = 3 = 2 + 1$

$2 + 5 = 7 = 5 + 2$

$7 + 1 = 8 = 1 + 7$

$3 + 1 = 4 = 1 + 3$

$2 + 8 = 10 = 8 + 2$

$8 + 1 = 9 = 1 + 8$

$2 + 3 = 5 = 3 + 2$

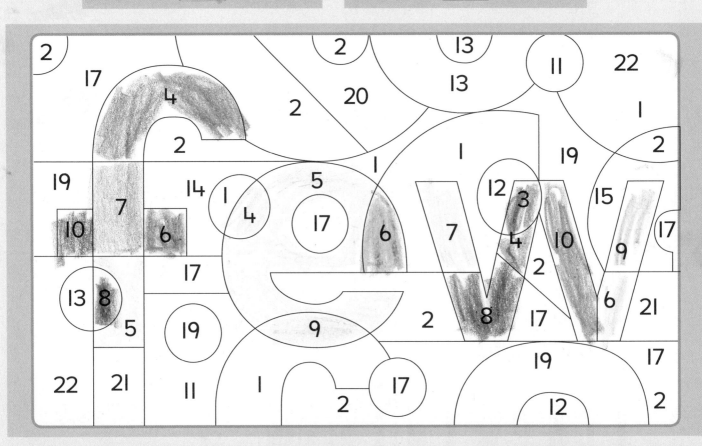

Ongoing Practice

I. Look at the graph.
Answer the questions.

Do you like bananas?

a. How many people like bananas? ⬚

b. How many people do not like bananas? ⬚

c. How many more people voted yes than no? ⬚

d. How many people voted in total? ⬚

Yes   No

2. Draw the same number of dots on the other end of the domino.
Then complete the equations to match.

a.

⬚ + ⬚ = ⬚

double ⬚ = ⬚

b.

⬚ + ⬚ = ⬚

double ⬚ = ⬚

Preparing for Module 3

What number am I? Use the number track to help your thinking.

| I | 2 | 3 | 4 | 5 | 6 | 7 | 8 | 9 | 10 | II | 12 | 13 | 14 | 15 | 16 | 17 | 18 | 19 | 20 |

a. My number has I ten and 5 ones.

⬚

b. My number is 3 less than 7.

⬚

Step In

Look at these analog clocks.

Which clocks show a time on the hour?

How do you know?

What time does this clock show?

How do you know?

Step Up

1. Read the time. Draw a ⏝ on the clock if it shows the same time. Draw a ⏜ on the clock if it shows a different time.

a. 3 o'clock

b. 7 o'clock

c. 5 o'clock

d. 2 o'clock

e. 6 o'clock

f. 10 o'clock

2. Draw hands on the clock to show the time.

a. 9 o'clock

b. 5 o'clock

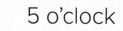

c. 1 o'clock

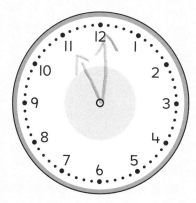

d. 11 o'clock

e. 6 o'clock

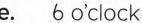

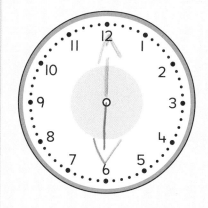

f. 4 o'clock

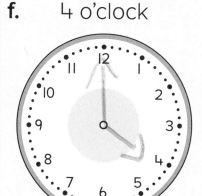

Step Ahead Copy the list words to show what you would be doing at each of these morning times.

sleeping   at school   eating breakfast   watching television

At 2 o'clock in the morning I am Sleeping

At 7 o'clock in the morning I am eating

At 10 o'clock in the morning I am

Step In

This type of clock is called a digital clock. How is this clock different from an analog clock?

The two dots between the numbers is called a **colon**.

What does the number on the left side of the colon show?
What do the numbers on the right side show?

What do you know about the time on this clock?
What time is the clock showing?

Step Up

1. Draw a line to join each digital clock and each analog clock to a matching label.

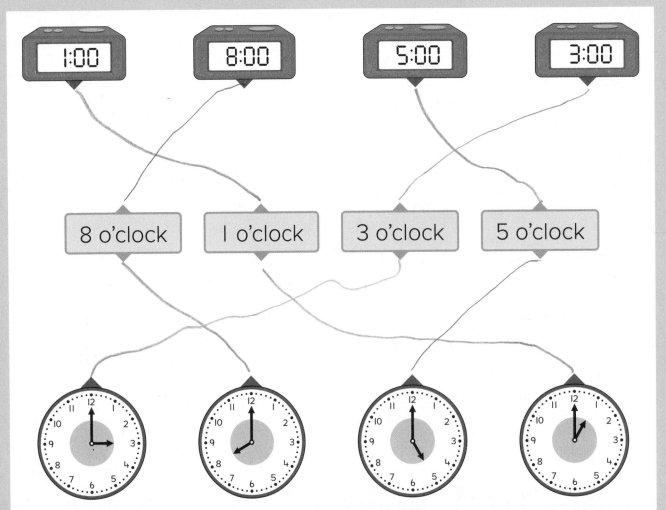

2. Write each time on the digital clock.

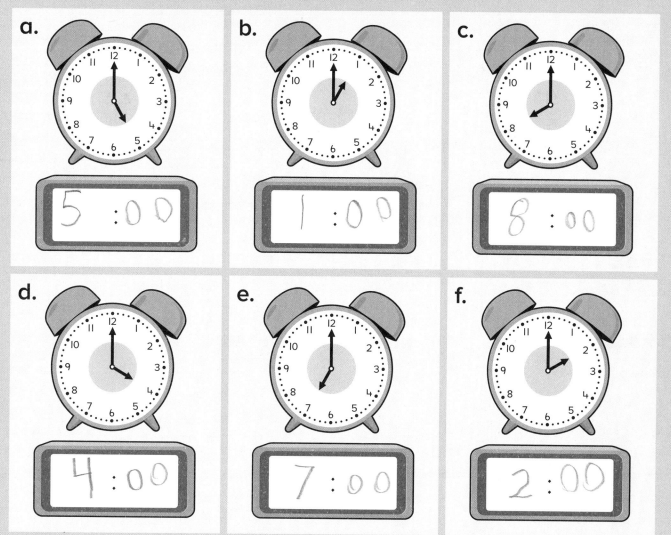

a. 5:00

b. 1:00

c. 8:00

d. 4:00

e. 7:00

f. 2:00

Step Ahead Look at each analog clock. Write the time that is **one hour before** and **one hour after**.

a. **one hour before**

6:00

one hour after

8:00

b. **one hour before**

2:00

one hour after
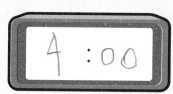
4:00

Think and Solve Same shapes weigh the same.
Write the missing value inside each shape.

 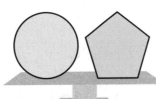   

10   12   6

Words at Work   **a.**   Write about a **double** you have seen at home.

b.   Draw a picture to show your **double**.

Ongoing Practice

1. This table shows how many grapes students can hold in one hand.

Student		
Athena	ᚋᚋ ᚋᚋ	
Riku	ᚋᚋ |||	
Alicia	ᚋᚋ ||||	

Draw ⭕ in the graph to show the data.

Number of Grapes We Can Hold

⭕ means I grape

Student											
Athena											
Riku											
Alicia											

2. Write each time.

a.

____ o'clock

b.

____ o'clock

c.
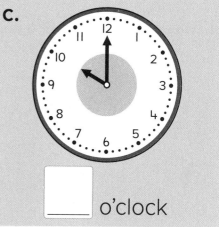
____ o'clock

Preparing for Module 3

Color the pictures blue if they are **shorter** than the string. Color the pictures yellow if they are **longer** than the string.

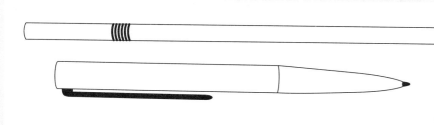
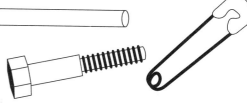

$$10 \times 10 = 100$$

ORIGO Stepping Stones • Grade 1 • Module 2

Step In Look at these number names.

| sixteen | eighteen | seventeen |

What does the **teen** part mean?

16 18 17

Look at these number names.

What does the **ty** part mean?

| sixty | eighty | seventy |

60 80 10

Look at these pairs of number names.
What do you notice?

| four | and | forty | | two | and | twenty |

| five | and | fifty | | three | and | thirty |

Step Up 1. Count by tens. Write the missing number names.

a.

| ten | twenty | Thity | forty |

b.

| thirty | Forty | fifty | sixty |

c.

| forty | fifty | Six Ty | seventy |

d.

| sixty | Sevnty | ei | ninety |

2. Circle each group of ten. Write the number of tens.
Then write the number name.

a. 2 tens __Twe__

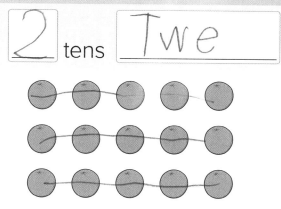

b. ___ tens _____

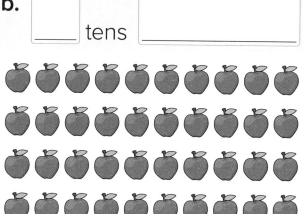

c. 6 tens __60__

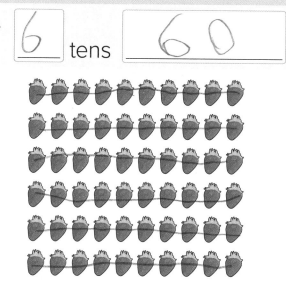

d. 3 tens __30__

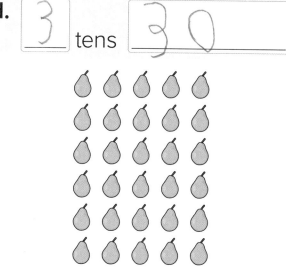

| Step Ahead | All these number names are spelled incorrectly. Write each word to show the correct spelling to match the names on page 82. |

a.   ninty

b.   fourty

c.   fivety

d.   thrity

Step In These are different ways of showing tens and ones.

What number does each picture show? How do you know?

24

24

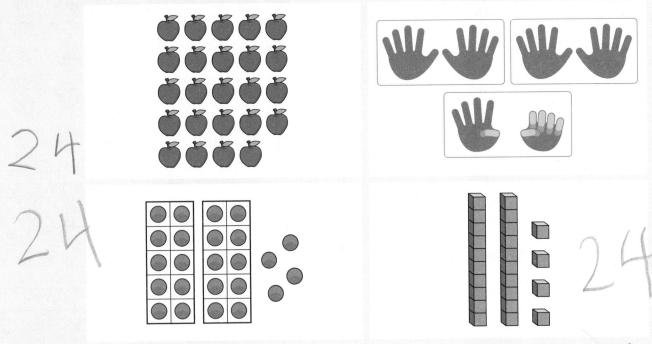

24

Where are the groups of ten in each picture?
Where are the extra ones?

**How would you write the number
of tens and ones on this expander
to show the same number?**

24

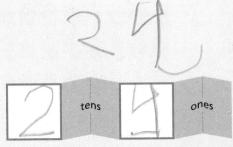

| 2 | tens | 4 | ones |

Step Up **I.** Write the matching number of tens and ones
on the expander.

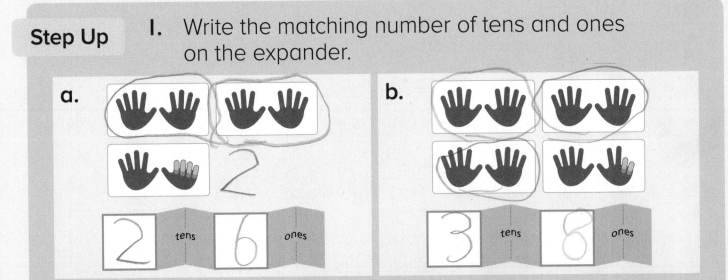

a.

2

| 2 | tens | 6 | ones |

b.

| 3 | tens | 8 | ones |

2. Write the matching number of tens and ones.

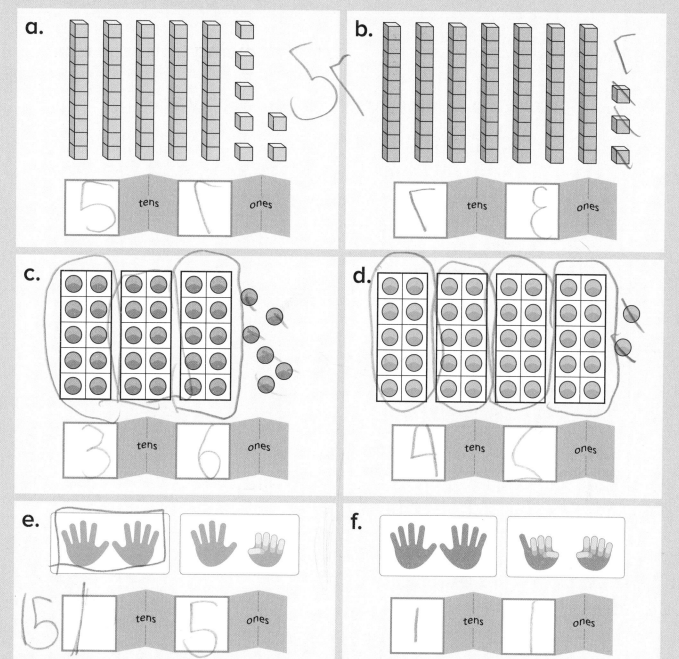

a.

5 tens   7 ones

b.

5 tens   3 ones

c.

3 tens   6 ones

d.

4 tens   5 ones

e.

5 tens   5 ones

f.

1 tens   1 ones

Step Ahead   Write the number of tens and ones on the expander.

a.   six tens and seven ones

6 tens   7 ones

b.   nine ones and three tens

3 tens   9 ones

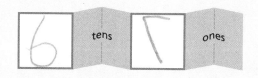

Computation Practice

★ Figure out which equations are true.

★ Color these triangles so the puma can see the path home.

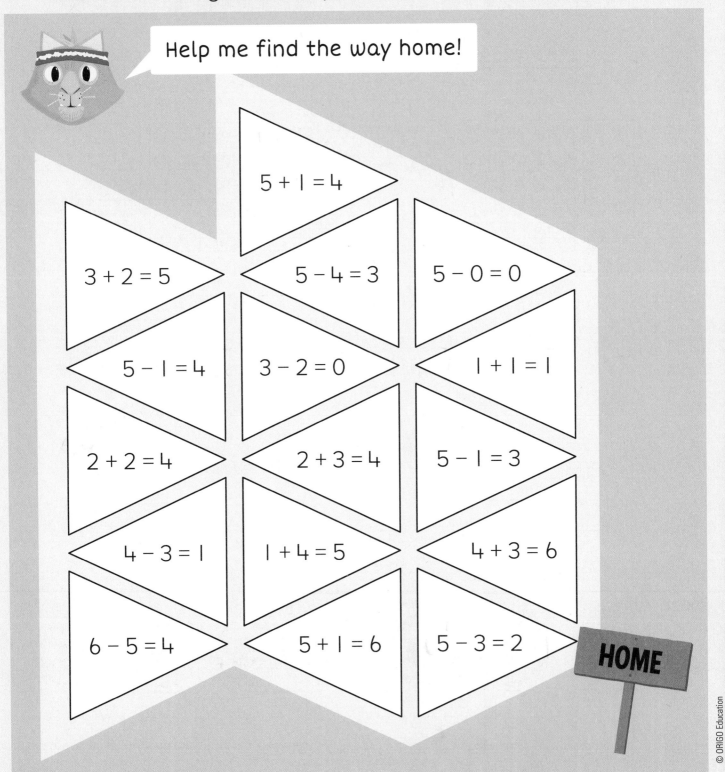

Help me find the way home!

$5 + 1 = 4$

$3 + 2 = 5$ $5 - 4 = 3$ $5 - 0 = 0$

$5 - 1 = 4$ $3 - 2 = 0$ $1 + 1 = 1$

$2 + 2 = 4$ $2 + 3 = 4$ $5 - 1 = 3$

$4 - 3 = 1$ $1 + 4 = 5$ $4 + 3 = 6$

$6 - 5 = 4$ $5 + 1 = 6$ $5 - 3 = 2$

HOME

Ongoing Practice

1. Start at 5 and count on. Write the total.

a.

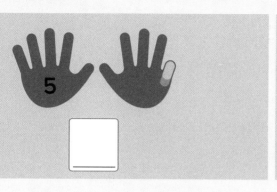

5

☐
___

b.

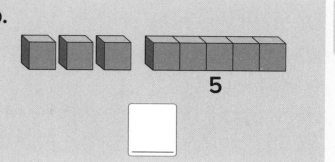

5

☐
___

2. Count by tens. Write the missing number names.

a.

twenty	thirty		fifty

b.

sixty	seventy	eighty	

Preparing for Module 4

Cross out the number shown.
Then complete the equation.

a.

7 balls

$\boxed{7}$ less $\boxed{1}$ = $\boxed{}$

b.

6 balls

$\boxed{}$ subtract $\boxed{2}$ = $\boxed{}$

Step In

Read the number on each expander.

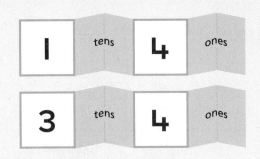

What do you notice?

When do you say the four ones in each number?

Think about how you would write these numbers in words. When would you write the four ones?

Step Up

1. Look at the number of counters on and off the frames. Write the matching number on the expander. Then complete the number name.

a.
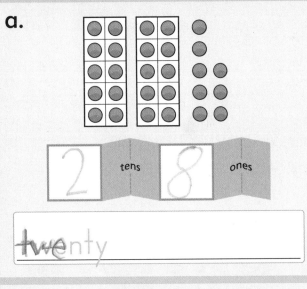

2 tens   8 ones

twenty

b.

3 tens   5 ones

thirty

c.
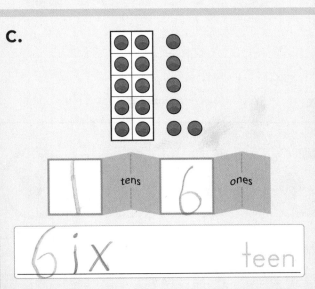

1 tens   6 ones

six   teen

d.

4 tens   1 ones

forty   One

2. Write the matching number on the expander.
Then write the number name.

a.

[3] tens [9] ones

thirty

b.

[1] tens [4] ones

for   teen

c.

[2] tens [3] ones

twenty   trhee

d.

[1] tens [9] ones

Nih   teen

Step Ahead | Read the number name.
Write the matching number on the expander.

a. seventeen

[1] tens [7] ones

b. sixty-three

[6] tens [3] ones

c. twelve

[1] tens [2] ones

d. ninety-two

[9] tens [2] ones

e. seventy-two

[7] tens [2] ones

f. fifty-seven

[5] tens [7] ones

Step In   **What number does this picture show?**

How do you know?

How would you write the number on this expander?

How would you write the number name?

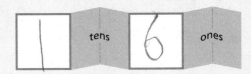

Six teen

What number does this picture show?

How do you know?

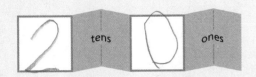

How would you write the number on this expander?

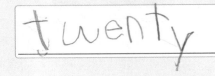

twenty

How would you write the number name?

Look at these number names.

How many tens are in these numbers? How do you know?

ten	eleven	twelve	thirteen	fourteen	fifteen
	sixteen	seventeen	eighteen	nineteen	

How are these numbers different from the numbers above?

twenty	thirty	forty	fifty
sixty	seventy	eighty	ninety	too

Step Up

Write the matching number of tens and ones on the expander. Then write the matching number name.

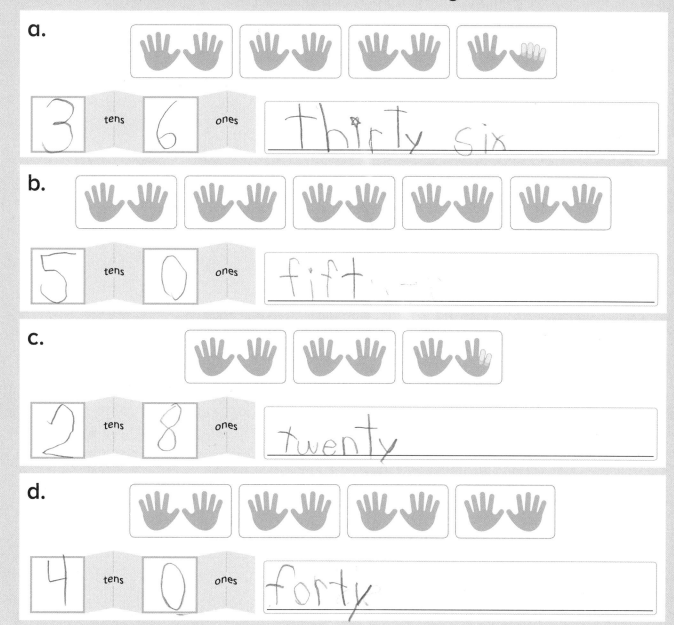

a. | 3 | tens | 6 | ones | thirty six

b. | 5 | tens | 0 | ones | fift__

c. | 2 | tens | 8 | ones | twenty

d. | 4 | tens | 0 | ones | forty

Step Ahead

Look at the number of tens and ones.
Write the matching number on the expander.

a. one ten and four ones

b. eight tens and six ones

© ORIGO Education

Think and Solve The same shapes weigh the same.

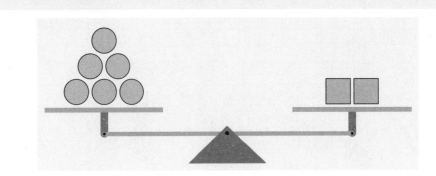

a. How many ◯ balance one ▢ ? ____

b. How many ◯ balance four ▢ ? _____

Words at Work Choose and write a word from the list to complete each sentence below. Each word is used only once.

| ones |
| sixty |
| one |
| tens |
| sixteen |
| seven |
| fifty |

a. _____ has one ten and six ones.

b. Thirty has three _____ and no ones.

c. Seventeen has _____ ones and _____ ten.

d. Twelve and thirty-two both have two _____.

e. When you start at 10 and count by tens, _____ comes after _____.

I. Figure out the total. Write the addition fact.

a.

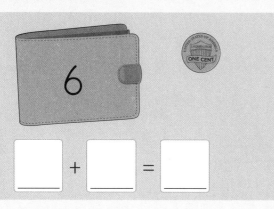

☐ + ☐ = ☐

b.

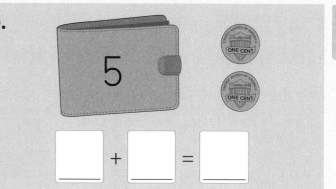

☐ + ☐ = ☐

FROM 1.2.4

2. Write the number on the expander.
Then complete the number name.

a.

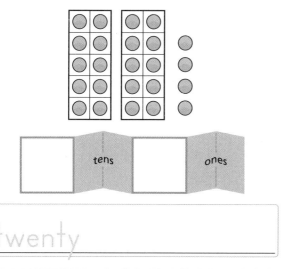

☐ tens ☐ ones

twenty

b.

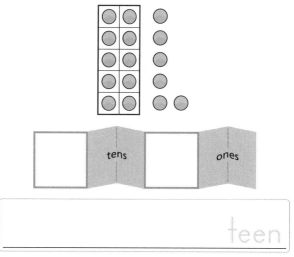

☐ tens ☐ ones

teen

FROM 1.3.3

Preparing for Module 4

Complete each equation to match
the picture.

a.

☐ less ☐ = ☐

b.

☐ subtract ☐ = ☐

© ORIGO Education

Step In Look at this picture of blocks.

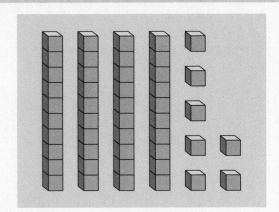

How many tens blocks are there?

How many ones blocks are there?

What number does it show?

How would you write the number
on this open expander?

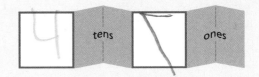

How would you write the same
number on these expanders?

How would you write the matching numeral
without an expander?

Step Up l. Write the matching number of tens and ones
on the open and closed expanders.

a.

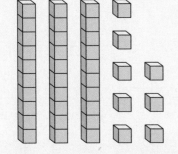

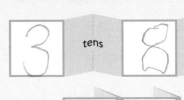

b.

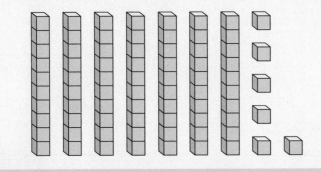

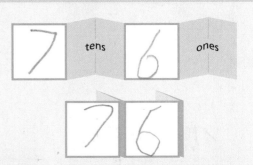

2. Write the number of tens and ones on the open expander.
Then write the matching number.

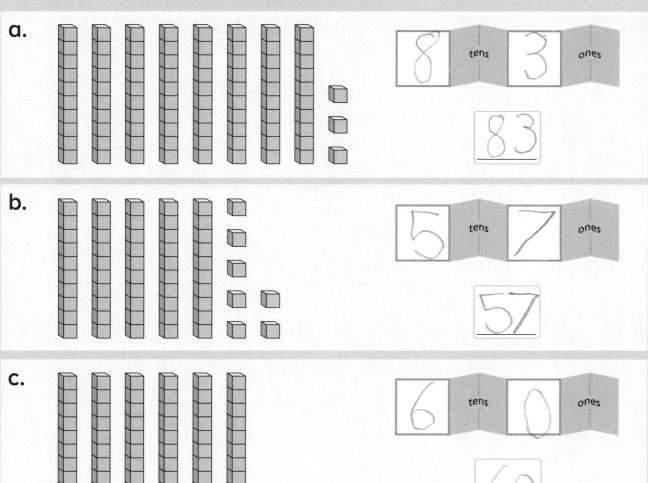

a.

| 8 | tens | 3 | ones |

83

b.

| 5 | tens | 7 | ones |

57

c.

| 6 | tens | 0 | ones |

60

a.
94

b.
12

c.
36   thir

© ORIGO Education

Step In Look at these items. What do you notice?

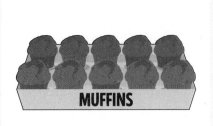

What are some other things that are in groups of 10?

How many marbles are in this pack?

How do you know?

How could you show 48 marbles?

I would use 4 packs of 10 plus 8 more marbles.

Step Up 1. Draw packs of 10 and some more marbles to match the number on the expander.

a.

| 2 | 4 |

b.

| 4 | 1 |

2. Draw packs of 10 and some more marbles to match the numeral. Then write the number name.

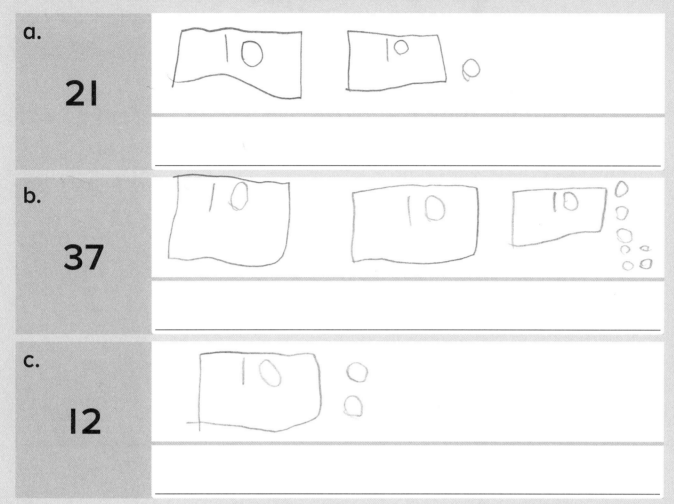

a. **21**	
b. **37**	
c. **12**	

Step Ahead

Franco's teacher is making a name badge for each student in the class. There are 25 students in the class. The name badges are sold in packs of 10.

How many packs of badges will the teacher need to buy? Draw a picture to show the answer.

NAME BADGES
10 PACK

Computation Practice   **Why do tigers eat raw meat?**

★ Complete the equations.

★ Write the letter in each box above its matching total at the bottom of the page. Some letters are used more than once.

$9 + 1 =$ 10 e $1 + 13 =$ 14 s

$2 + 13 =$ 15 h $1 + 4 =$ 5 a

$1 + 7 =$ 8 n $2 + 1 =$ 3 u

$3 + 1 =$ 4 t $10 + 2 =$ 12 b

$19 + 1 =$ 20 y $6 + 1 =$ 7 c

$8 + 1 =$ 9 o $2 + 4 =$ 6 k

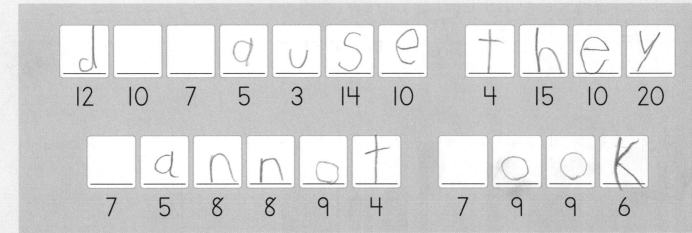

b		c	a	u	s	e		t	h	e	y
12	10	7	5	3	14	10		4	15	10	20

	c	a	n	n	o	t		c	o	o	k
7	5	8	8	9	4		7	9	9	6

© ORIGO Education

I. Complete the addition fact and its turnaround fact.

a.
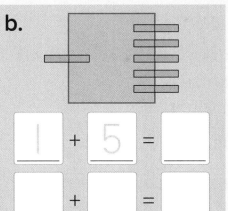

3 + 2 = ☐

2 + ☐ = ☐

b.

1 + 5 = ☐

☐ + ☐ = ☐

c.
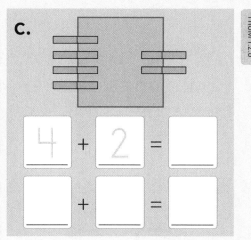

4 + 2 = ☐

☐ + ☐ = ☐

2. Write the matching number of tens and ones on the expander. Then write the number name.

a.

☐ tens ☐ ones

b.

☐ tens ☐ ones

Write the total. Cover 1 or 2 dots. Then write the number that is left.

a.

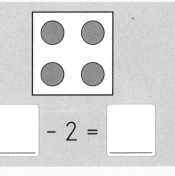

☐ − 2 = ☐

b.

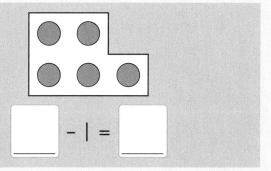

☐ − 1 = ☐

Step In Look at these coins.

How many pennies do you see?
How many cents is one penny worth?

How many dimes do you see?
How many cents is one dime worth?

How would you write the matching number of tens and ones on this expander?

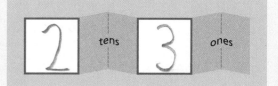

How do you know?

How would you show the same amount on these expanders?

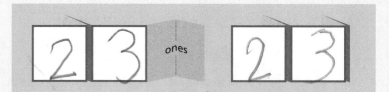

What numeral would you write?

Step Up   I.   Write the number of dimes and pennies.

a.

There are 3 dimes and 4 pennies.

b.

There are 4 dimes and 2 pennies.

2. Write the number of dimes and pennies. Then write the matching numeral with and without the expander.

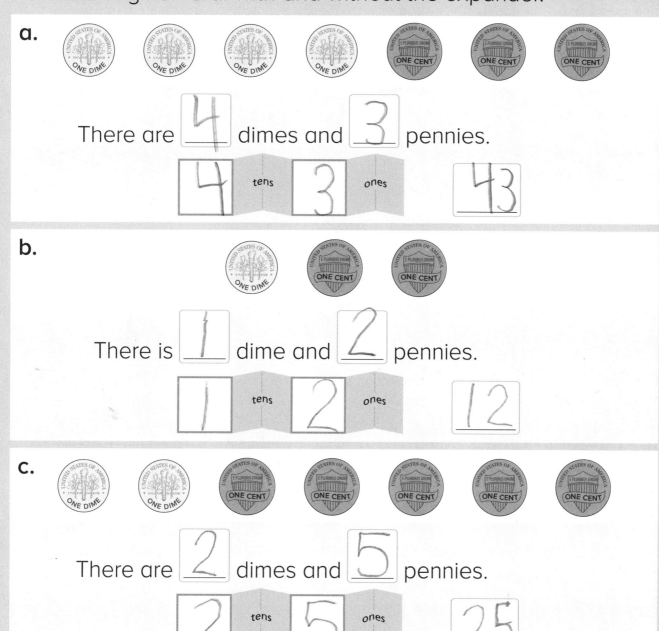

a. There are **4** dimes and **3** pennies.

4 tens **3** ones **43**

b. There is **1** dime and **2** pennies.

1 tens **2** ones **12**

c. There are **2** dimes and **5** pennies.

2 tens **5** ones **25**

Step Ahead Write the total number of cents in words.

ford tow cents

© ORIGO Education

3.8 Number: Solving puzzles

Step In

Victoria puts out these blocks to match a set of clues. What number does she show?

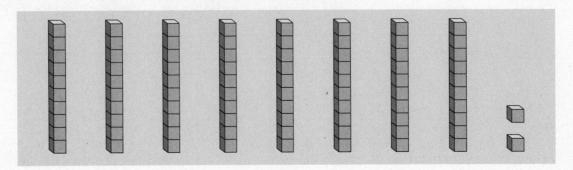

Circle the set of clues she followed.

| ~~I have more tens blocks than ones blocks.~~ ~~My number name starts with **twenty**.~~ | ~~I have more ones blocks than tens blocks.~~ ~~My number name starts with **eighty**.~~ | I have more tens blocks than ones blocks. My number name starts with **eighty**. |

What other numbers could be shown to match the clues that Victoria followed?

Step Up

I. Color the tens and ones blocks to match the clues. There is more than one possible answer.

My number name starts with **fifty**.

I have more ones blocks than tens blocks.

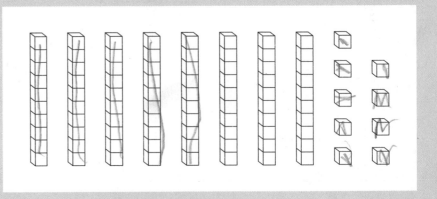

2. Use tens and ones blocks to act out these clues.
Then write the matching number.

a. My number has
7 tens blocks and
2 ones blocks.

72

b. My number has
8 ones blocks
and 3 tens blocks.

83

c. My number has
6 ones blocks
and 0 tens blocks.

60

3. Write three different numerals to match each set of clues.
You can use blocks to help.

a. My number has the same
number of tens blocks as
ones blocks. My number
has two digits.

44 55 66

b. My number has more tens
blocks than ones blocks.
My number name starts
with **forty**.

40 41 42

c. My number has more ones
blocks than tens blocks.
My number name ends
with **teen**.

13 13 14

d. My number has fewer tens
blocks than ones blocks.
My number name starts
with **twenty**.

24 25 26

Step Ahead List all the numbers that you could write
for Question 3a.

23 24 ☐ ☐ ☐ ☐ ☐ ☐ ☐

Think and Solve   THE THINK TANK

a. How many dots are inside this shape? _____

b. How many dots are on the sides of this shape? _____

c. Draw a different shape that has the same number of sides with 2 dots on the inside.

Words at Work   Write some clues to match the number 64. You can use words from the list to help you.

| tens |
| ones |
| same |
| number |
| number name |
| starts with |
| ends with |

I. Write doubles you know to figure out these.

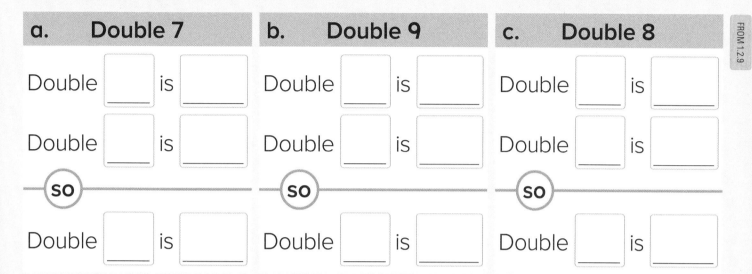

a.	Double 7	b.	Double 9	c.	Double 8

Double ☐ is ☐   Double ☐ is ☐   Double ☐ is ☐

Double ☐ is ☐   Double ☐ is ☐   Double ☐ is ☐

SO   **SO**   **SO**

Double ☐ is ☐   Double ☐ is ☐   Double ☐ is ☐

FROM 1.2.9

2. Write the number of dimes and pennies. Then write the matching numeral with and without the expander.

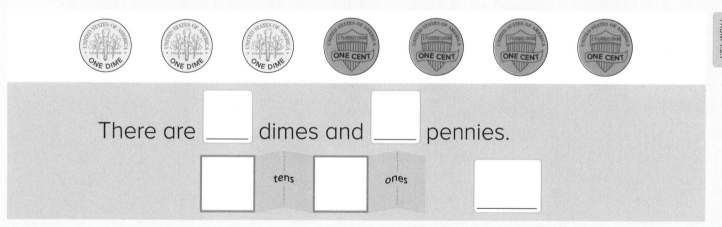

There are ☐ dimes and ☐ pennies.

☐ tens ☐ ones   ☐

FROM 1.3.7

Write an equation to solve each problem.

a. There are 7 fish in the tank. One fish is hiding. How many fish can be seen?

b. There are 2 horses and 3 cows on a farm. How many animals are there in total?

Step In   Three friends make bracelets from paper strips.

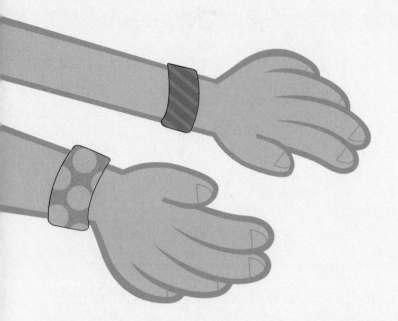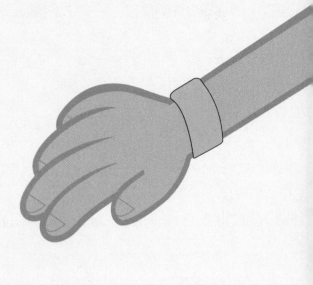

They take them off and notice that they are different lengths.

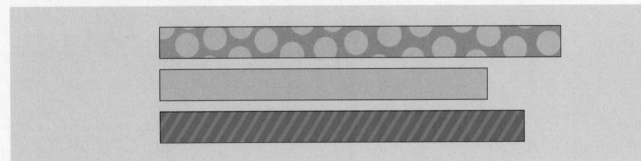

Describe the length of each bracelet.

Say the patterns of the bracelets in order from shortest to longest.

What pattern bracelet belongs to the student with the smallest wrist? How do you know?

Step Up   I.   Follow these instructions.

a.   With your teacher's help, make three paper strip bracelets.

b.   Write your name on each bracelet.

c. Paste your bracelet and the bracelet of two other students below.

2. Write student names to make these statements true.

a. _____ has the longest bracelet.

b. _____ has the shortest bracelet.

3. Order the students' names from **shortest** to **longest** bracelet.

Step Ahead Look at these strips. Color the ⬭ beside the statement that is true.

○ Striped is longer than dotted.
○ Dotted is shorter than plain.
○ Dotted and plain are the same length.

Step In   Imagine that you straightened each piece of string.

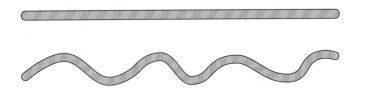 

Which piece of string do you think would be longest?
How do you know?

How could you measure the length of each piece
of string to check your estimate?

I could bend a real piece of
string to measure each length.

Step Up   I. Use string to compare the length of each pencil.
Write **L** beside the pencil that is longer in each pair.

a.
)
Sh

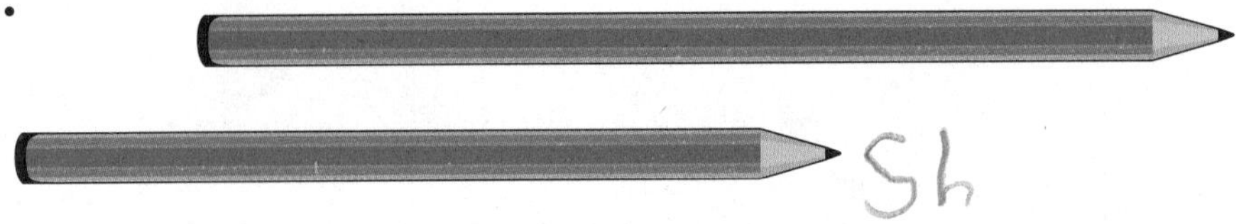

b.
I
Sh

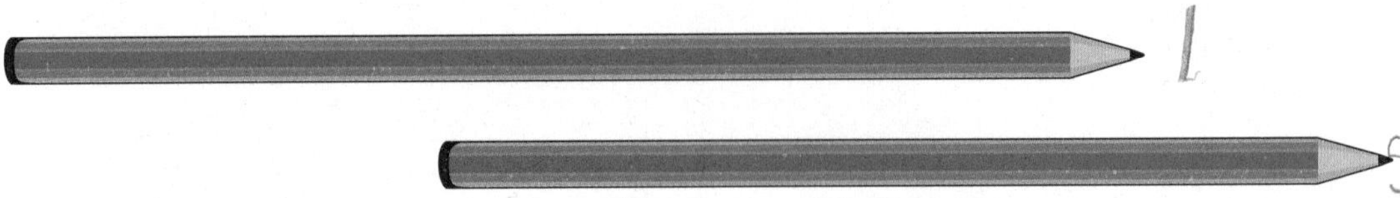

c. 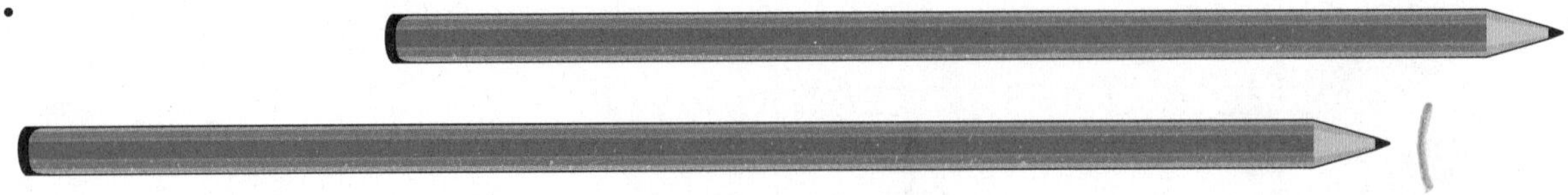
Sh
(

© ORIGO Education

2. Use the string to compare the length of each side of each triangle. Then color the **longest** side of each triangle.

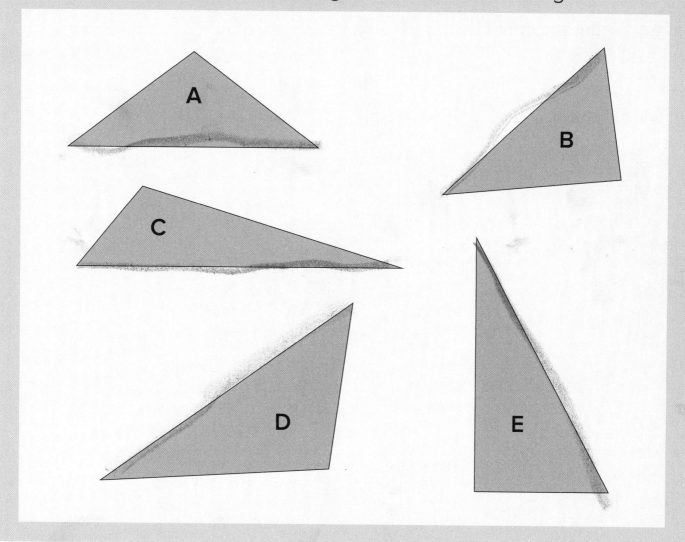

Step Ahead Circle the piece of string that is the longest.

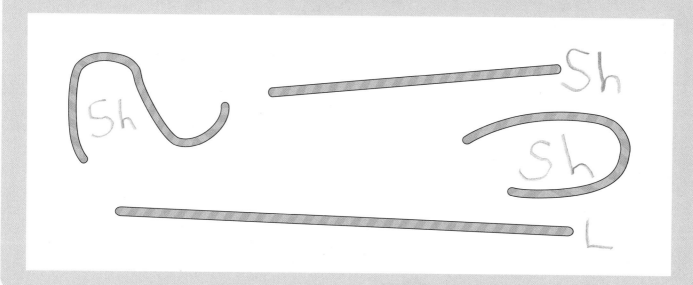

© ORIGO Education

Computation Practice

★ Add the number in the star to each number in the circles.

★ Write the totals in the squares.

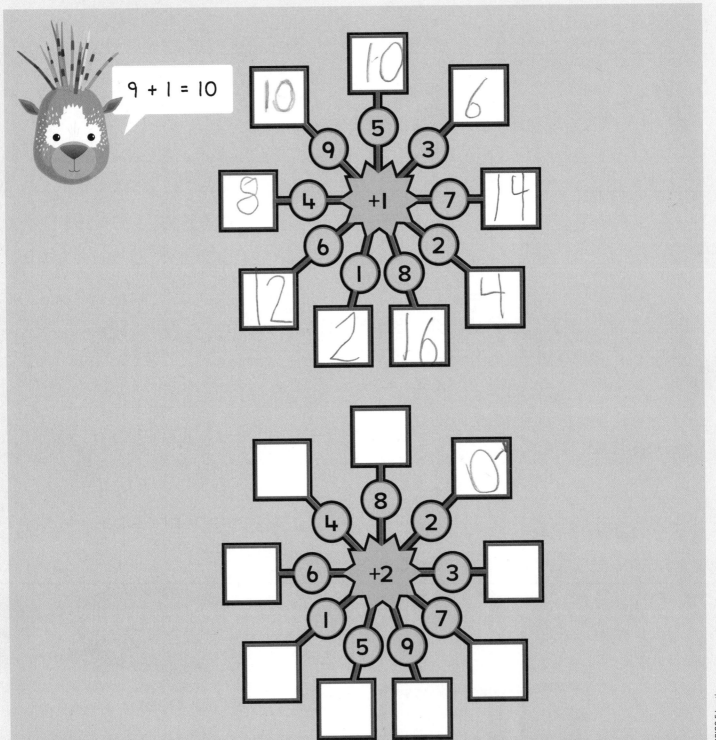

9 + 1 = 10

Ongoing Practice

I. The **minute** hand is the **long** hand. Draw the minute hand on each clock to show an hour time. Then write the time.

a.

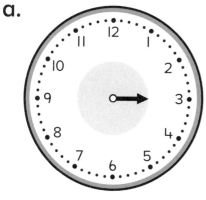

b.

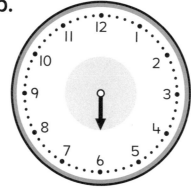

c.

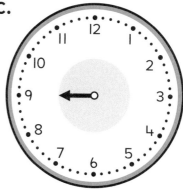

☐ o'clock   ☐ o'clock   ☐ o'clock

2. Color tens and ones blocks to match the clues. There is more than one possible answer.

My number name starts with **sixty**.

I have more tens blocks than ones blocks.

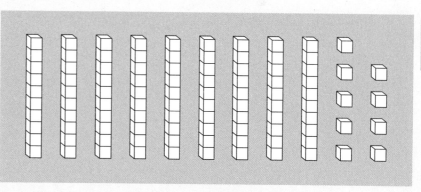

Preparing for Module 4

Count and write the number of sides and corners for each shape.

a.

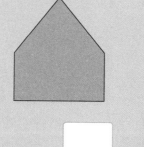

☐ sides   ☐ corners

b.

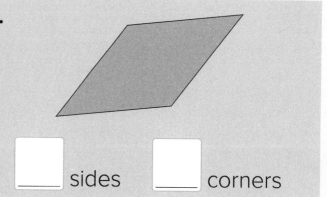

☐ sides   ☐ corners

Step In

How could you use the cubes to measure the length of the pencil?

Does it matter which way the cubes are placed? Why?

Does it matter if gaps are left between the cubes? Why?

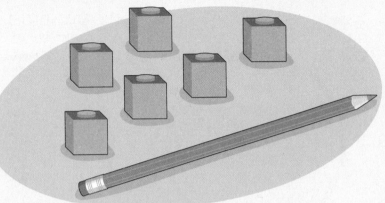

Step Up

I. Color the objects that are about the same length as the cube train.

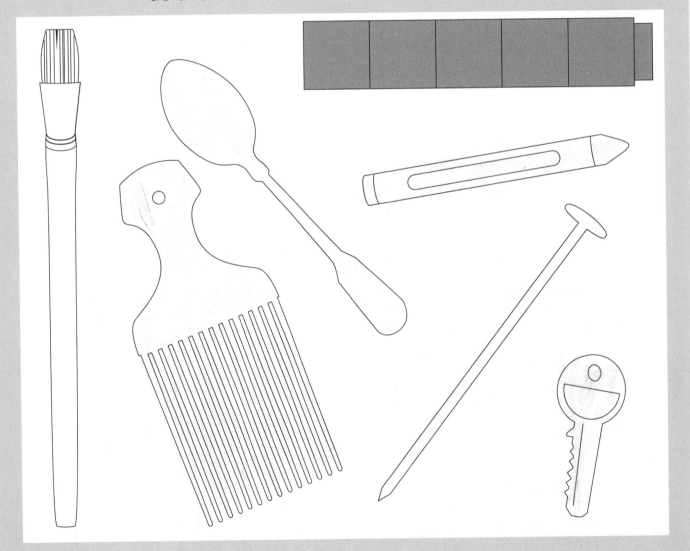

2. Color the objects that are about the same length as the cube train.

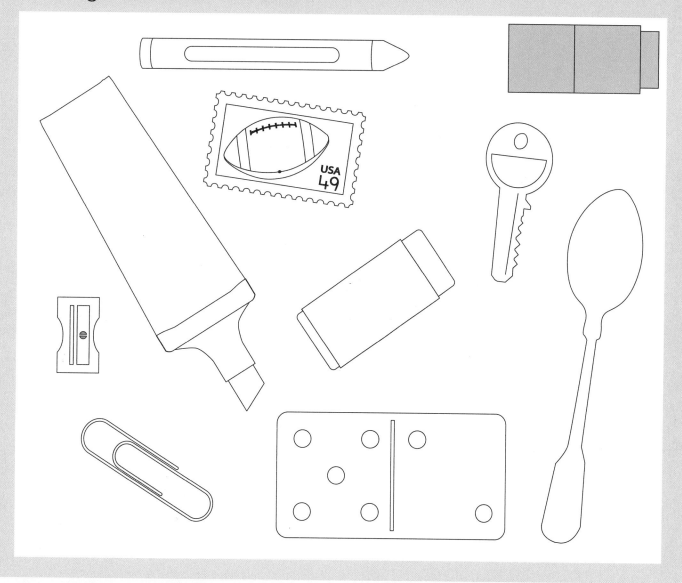

Step Ahead   List some more classroom objects that are about **5 cubes long**.

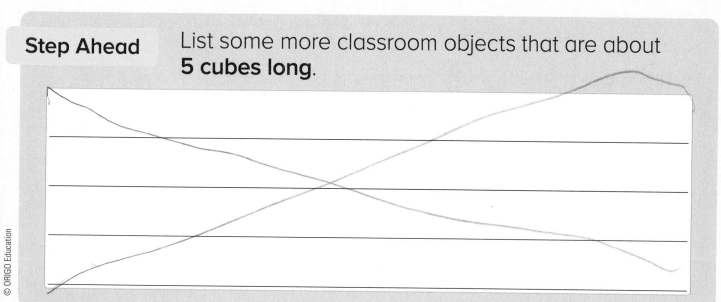

Step In Paper ants were used to measure this straw.

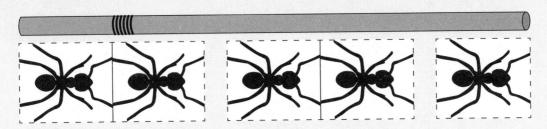

Is the measurement accurate? How do you know?

How would you use paper ants to measure the straw?

I would use tape to join my paper ants so they are in one line with no gaps or overlaps.

Jayden used paper ants to measure this straw.
What mistake did he make?

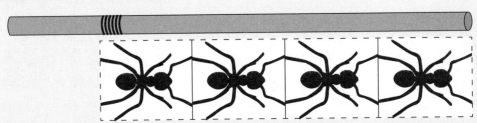

Step Up I. Use your paper ant trail to measure each straw. Write the number of ants.

a.

5 ants long

b.

3 ants long

c.

4 ants long

2. Use red to color the straws that are 4 ants long.
Use blue to color the straws that are 6 ants long.
There are some straws left over.

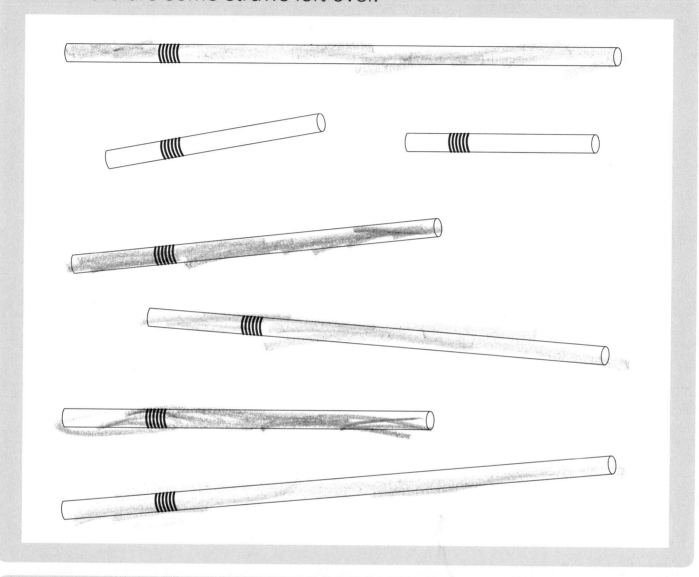

Step Ahead   Color the straw that is three ants long.

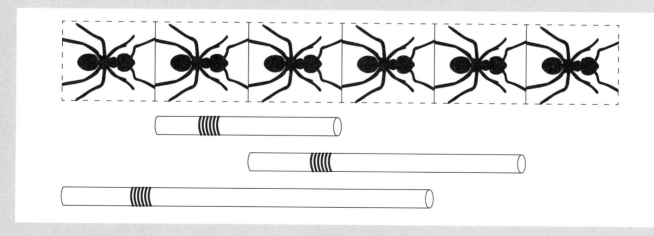

Think and Solve Joel and Amos have 12 toy cars in total. Joel has 2 more toy cars than Amos.

a. How many toy cars does Joel have?

b. How many does Amos have?

c. How many toy cars could Joel give to Amos so that they each have the same number?

Words at Work Write about the **length** of these pencils. You can use words from the list to help you.

| white |
| blue |
| long |
| longer |
| short |
| shorter |
| length |

1. Write each time on the digital clock.

a.

b.
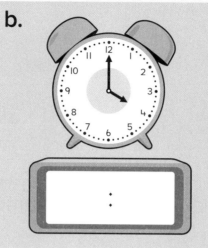

c.

FROM 1.2.12

2. Color the **longest** ribbon blue. Color the **shortest** ribbon red.

FROM 1.3.9

Preparing for Module 4   Copy the picture.

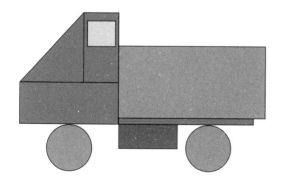

| Step In | There are seven fish in the tank.
Color some of the fish orange. |

Complete the equation to show the number of fish that are **not** orange.

$$7 - 3 = 4$$

How does each number in the equation match the picture of fish in the tank?

How many different equations could you write?

| Step Up | I. Complete each equation. |

a.

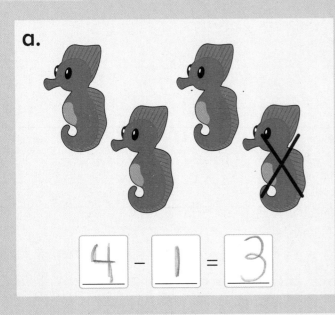

$$4 - 1 = 3$$

b.

$$5 - 2 = 3$$

ORIGO Stepping Stones · Grade 1 · 4.1

© ORIGO Education

2. Write the equation to match the picture.

a.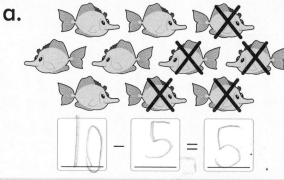

$\boxed{10} - \boxed{5} = \boxed{5}$

b.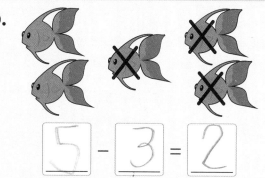

$\boxed{5} - \boxed{3} = \boxed{2}$

c.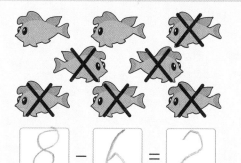

$\boxed{8} - \boxed{6} = \boxed{2}$

d.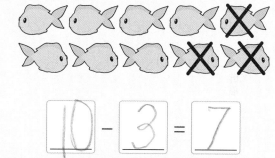

$\boxed{10} - \boxed{3} = \boxed{7}$

e.

$\boxed{7} - \boxed{2} = \boxed{5}$

f.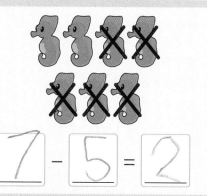

$\boxed{7} - \boxed{5} = \boxed{2}$

Step Ahead Write numbers to complete seven **different** equations.

$6 - \boxed{} = \boxed{}$ $6 - \boxed{} = \boxed{}$ $6 - \boxed{} = \boxed{}$

$6 - \boxed{} = \boxed{}$ $6 - \boxed{} = \boxed{}$

$6 - \boxed{} = \boxed{}$ $6 - \boxed{} = \boxed{}$

Step In   What is happening in this picture?

What is the total number of hens?

How many hens are leaving the pen?

How many hens will be left in the pen?

Complete this equation to match the picture.

$9 - 2 = 7$

Step Up   I. Write the total number of hens. **Cross out** the hens that run away. Write the number of hens left.

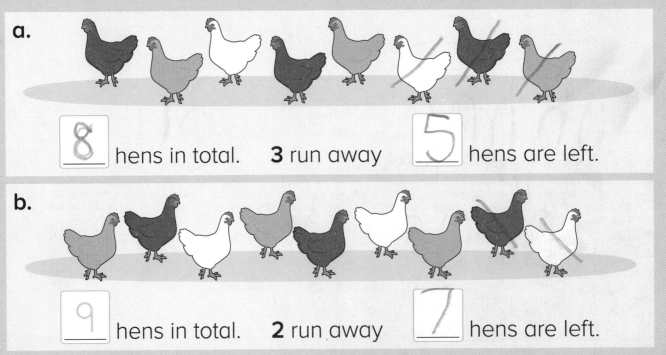

a.

8 hens in total.   **3 run away**   5 hens are left.

b.

9 hens in total.   **2 run away**   7 hens are left.

2. Complete the equation to match each picture.

a.

$\boxed{5} - \boxed{2} = \boxed{3}$

b.

$\boxed{6} - \boxed{3} = \boxed{3}$

c.

$\boxed{7} - \boxed{3} = \boxed{4}$

d.

$\boxed{5} - \boxed{4} = \boxed{1}$

Step Ahead

a. Write some numbers to show a subtraction fact.

$\boxed{} - \boxed{} = \boxed{}$

b. Draw a picture to match.

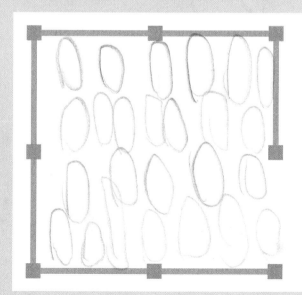

30 - 5 = 25

Computation Practice

★ Complete the equations.

★ Find each total in the puzzle below and color it to match.

$5 - 4 = \boxed{1}$ yellow

$3 + 2 = \boxed{5}$ purple

$2 + 2 = \boxed{4}$ brown

$6 + 0 = \boxed{6}$ orange

$2 + 1 = \boxed{3}$ green

$4 + 3 = \boxed{7}$ red

$5 - 3 = \boxed{2}$ light blue

$8 + 2 = \boxed{10}$ dark blue

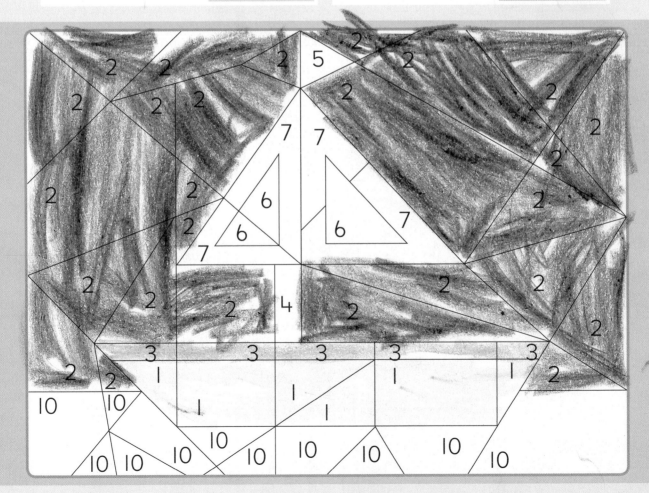

I. Count by tens. Write the missing number names.

a.

| ten | | thirty | forty |

FROM 1.3.1

b.

| forty | fifty | | seventy |

c.

| sixty | | eighty | |

2. Complete each equation.

a.

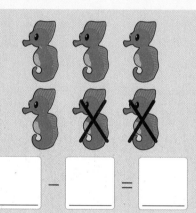

◻ – ◻ = ◻

b.

◻ – ◻ = ◻

FROM 1.4.1

Preparing for Module 5   Figure out each of these.

a. **Double 7**	b. **Double 9**	c. **Double 8**
Double 5 is ◻	Double 5 is ◻	Double 5 is ◻
Double 2 is ◻	Double 4 is ◻	Double 3 is ◻
(SO)	(SO)	(SO)
Double 7 is ◻	Double 9 is ◻	Double 8 is ◻

Step In   What is happening in this picture?

What is the total number of muffins?

How many muffins has Little Fox taken?

How many muffins are left on the tray?

Complete this equation to match the picture.

$12 - 4 = 8$

Step Up   1. Complete the equation to match each picture.

a.

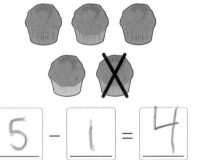

$5 - 1 = 4$

b.

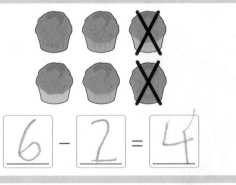

$6 - 2 = 4$

c.

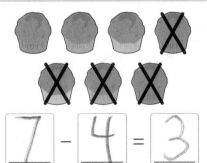

$7 - 4 = 3$

d.

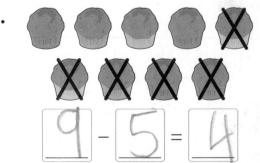

$9 - 5 = 4$

ORIGO Stepping Stones · Grade 1 · 4.3

© ORIGO Education

2. Cross out some of the muffins.
Then write an equation to match.

a.
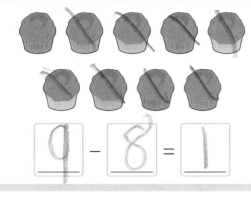
$9 - 8 = 1$

b.
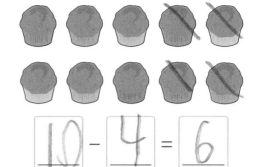
$10 - 4 = 6$

c.
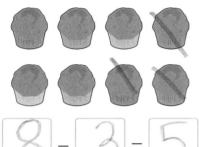
$8 - 3 = 5$

d.
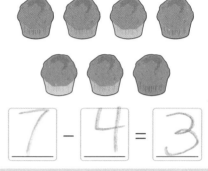
$7 - 4 = 3$

e.
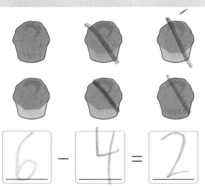
$6 - 4 = 2$

f.
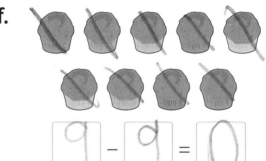
$9 - 9 = 0$

Step Ahead   Draw and cross out muffins on the tray to match this fact.

$5 - 5 = 0$

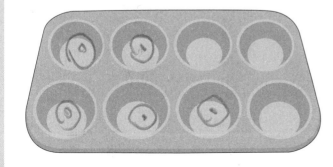

Step In   There are 10 cars in this parking lot.

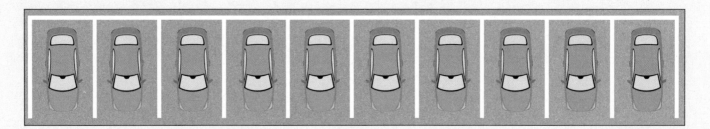

If 2 cars drive away, how many cars will be left?

I can count back from 10 to figure out the answer. That is **10, 9, 8,** so **8** cars will be left.

Bella showed her thinking on this number track.

| 1 | 2 | 3 | 4 | 5 | 6 | 7 | 8 | 9 | 10 |

Describe the steps that she followed.

Use the number track to figure out 5 – 2.

Write the matching equation.

$10 - 2 = 8$

Step Up   1.   Write the answers.

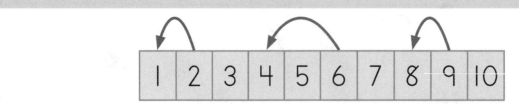

| 1 | 2 | 3 | 4 | 5 | 6 | 7 | 8 | 9 | 10 |

a. $2 - 1 = 1$

b. $6 - 2 = 4$

c. $9 - 1 = 8$

2. Write the answers. Draw jumps on the number track to help.

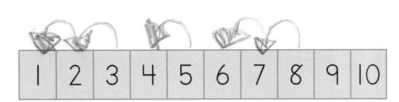

a. $5 - 1 = \boxed{4}$

b. $3 - 2 = \boxed{1}$

c. $8 - 2 = \boxed{6}$

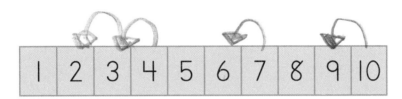

d. $4 - 2 = \boxed{2}$

e. $10 - 1 = \boxed{9}$

f. $7 - 1 = \boxed{6}$

g. $3 - 0 = \boxed{3}$

h. $6 - 1 = \boxed{5}$

i. $10 - 3 = \boxed{7}$

Step Ahead

There are 7 books on a shelf. Bianca takes 2 books to read. Callum takes 3 books. How many books are left on the shelf?

$\boxed{2}$ books

Think and Solve

You can only move ⟶ or ↑.

•⟶• is 1 unit.

How many units are in the **shortest** path from **A** to **B**? ☐

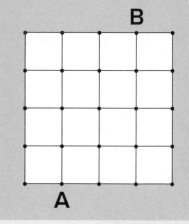

Words at Work

a. Write a subtraction story. You can use words from the list to help you.

subtract
equals
makes
left
total
group
how many

b. Draw a picture to match your story.

c. Write an equation to match.

☐ – ☐ = ☐

Ongoing Practice

I. Write the number of tens and ones on the expander.

FROM 1.3.2 + 1.3.4

a.

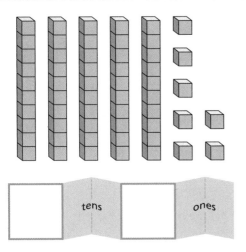

	tens		ones

b.

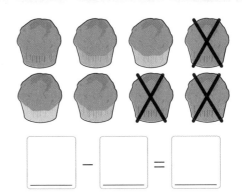

	tens		ones

2. Write an equation to match each picture.

FROM 1.4.3

a.

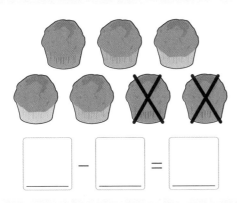

☐ – ☐ = ☐

b.

☐ – ☐ = ☐

Preparing for Module 5   Figure out each of these.

a. **Double 9**	b. **Double 8**	c. **Double 6**
Double 5 is ☐	Double 5 is ☐	Double 5 is ☐
Double 4 is ☐	Double 3 is ☐	Double 1 is ☐
SO	**SO**	**SO**
Double 9 is ☐	Double 8 is ☐	Double 6 is ☐

Step In

There are 7 blocks in the container. If 2 blocks are taken out, how many blocks will be left in the container?

Write an equation to show the blocks that will be left in the container.

$7 - 2 = 5$

Evan used a number track to solve a different equation.

| 1 | 2 | 3 | 4 | 5 | 6 | 7 | 8 | 9 | 10 |

Circle the equation that he solved.

$8 - 7 = 1$ $7 + 1 = 8$ $8 - 1 = 7$

How did you decide which equation to circle?

Step Up

1. Write the answers. Draw jumps on the number track to help you.

| 1 | 2 | 3 | 4 | 5 | 6 | 7 | 8 | 9 | 10 |

a. $5 - 1 = 4$ b. $4 - 0 = 4$ c. $9 - 2 = 7$

2. Write an equation to show the blocks that are left in the container.

a.

4 blocks

Take out **1**.

$4 - 1 = 3$

b.

6 blocks

Take out **2**.

$6 - 2 = 4$

c.

4 blocks

Take out **2**.

$4 - 2 = 2$

d.

7 blocks

Take out **0**.

$7 - 0 = 7$

e.

9 blocks

Take out **3**.

$9 - 3 = 6$

f.

2 blocks

Take out **2**.

$2 - 2 = 0$

3. Write the answers.

a. $3 - 1 = 2$

b. $7 - 2 = 5$

c. $10 - 0 = 10$

d. $8 - 3 = 6$

e. $5 - 1 = 4$

f. $8 - 2 = 7$

Step Ahead

4 birds are on a fence.
2 more birds join them.
Then one of the birds flies away.
How many birds are left sitting on the fence?

5 birds

Step In

This puzzle has 10 pieces.
Kuma takes out 2 pieces.
How many pieces are left in the box?

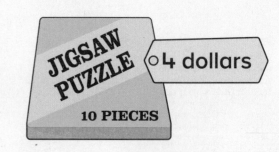

Write an equation to show your thinking.

$10 - 2 = 8$

This puzzle costs 4 dollars to buy.
Anya pays with a 5-dollar bill.
How much money should she get back?

Write an equation to show your thinking.

$5 - 4 = 1$

Step Up

1. Solve each problem. Draw pictures or write equations to show your thinking.

a. A box holds 8 puzzle pieces. 2 pieces are taken out of the box. How many pieces are left in the box?	b. There are 10 puzzle pieces on the floor. 3 pieces are blue. The rest are red. How many pieces are red?
 $8 - 2 = \boxed{6}$ pieces	 ___ pieces

2. Solve each problem. Show your thinking.

a. A puzzle has 8 pieces. 6 pieces have at least one straight edge. How many pieces do not have a straight edge?

 pieces

b. A puzzle has 8 pieces. Hernando needs 3 pieces to finish the puzzle. How many pieces has he already placed?

 pieces

c. A puzzle has 8 pieces. My little brother has lost some pieces. There are now 6 pieces in the box. How many pieces are lost?

 2 = 6 pieces

d. A puzzle costs 9 dollars. Henry and Anna share the cost. What amount could they each pay?

Anna 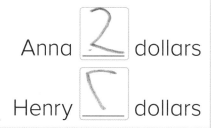 2 dollars

Henry dollars

Step Ahead

These puzzle pieces were left on the floor. The rest of the pieces were put back in the box. How many pieces are in the box?

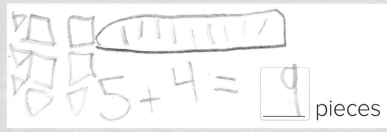 5 + 4 = 9 pieces

JIGSAW PUZZLE

9 PIECES

ORIGO Stepping Stones · Grade 1 · 4.6

© ORIGO Education

135 ◆

Computation Practice **Find what is hiding in the puzzle below.**

★ Complete the equations.

★ Color each total in the puzzle below.

$4 + 6 = \boxed{10} = 6 + 4$ $5 + 3 = \boxed{8} = 3 + 5$ $2 + 4 = \boxed{6} = 4 + 2$

$2 + 10 = \boxed{12} = 10 + 2$ $6 + 1 = \boxed{7} = 1 + 6$ $1 + 3 = \boxed{4} = 3 + 1$

$7 + 2 = \boxed{9} = 2 + 7$ $10 + 1 = \boxed{11} = 1 + 10$ $3 + 2 = \boxed{5} = 2 + 3$

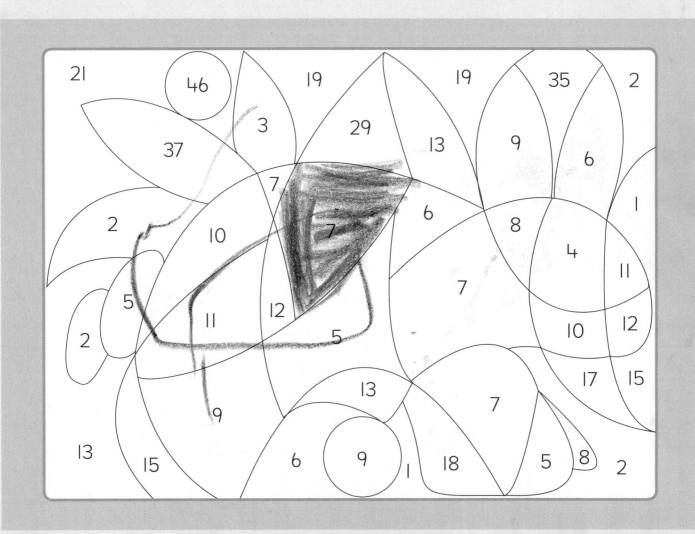

ORIGO Stepping Stones · Grade 1 · 4.6

© ORIGO Education

Ongoing Practice

1. Look at the counters. Write the matching number on the expander. Then complete the number name.

a.

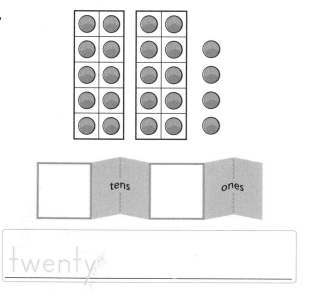

| | tens | | ones |

twenty

b.

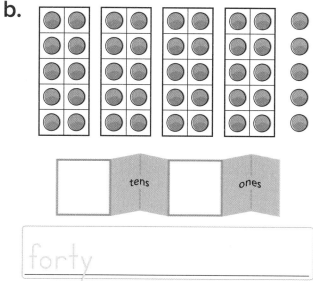

| | tens | | ones |

forty

2. Write the answers. Draw jumps on the number track to help you.

| 1 | 2 | 3 | 4 | 5 | 6 | 7 | 8 | 9 | 10 |

a.
$3 - 1 = \boxed{}$

b.
$5 - 2 = \boxed{}$

c.
$9 - 2 = \boxed{}$

Preparing for Module 5   Write the equation to match each card.

a.

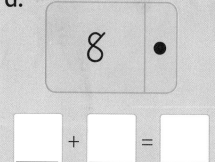

$\boxed{} + \boxed{} = \boxed{}$

b.

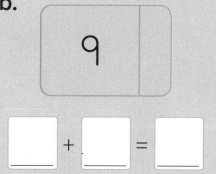

$\boxed{} + \boxed{} = \boxed{}$

c.

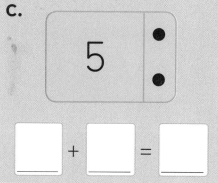

$\boxed{} + \boxed{} = \boxed{}$

Step In   Some friends are shopping in a fishing store.

They each have 10 dollars to spend. Which items could they buy?

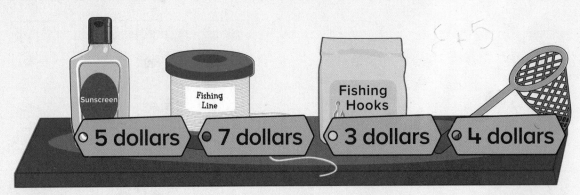

Chloe buys a pack of fishing hooks and a bottle of sunscreen. What amount does she spend?

She pays for the sunscreen and fishing hooks with a 10-dollar bill. How much money does she get back?

Marvin spends exactly 10 dollars. What items did he buy?

Step Up   1. Use the prices above. Solve each problem. Draw pictures or write equations to show your thinking.

a. Eva buys one net and one pack of hooks. How much does she spend?	**b.** Peter buys 2 bottles of sunscreen and one pack of hooks. What is the total cost?
$4 + 3 = 7$	$10 + 3 = 13$
 7 dollars	____ dollars

2. Solve each problem. Show your thinking.

a. There are 7 people fishing on the beach. Brady counts 4 girls. How many boys are fishing?

$7-4=3$ **3** boys

b. Kyle has sold 6 large fish and 6 small fish. He has 2 more fish left to sell. How many fish has he sold?

$6+6=12$ **12** fish

c. Lulu catches 5 fish. She gives away some fish and has 2 fish left. How many fish did she give away?

$5-5=3.$ **3** fish

d. 6 crabs are in a bucket. Some more crabs are put in to make a total of 9 crabs. How many more crabs were put in the bucket?

$6+3=9$ **9** crabs

Step Ahead   Circle two of these numbers. Use your numbers to write a subtraction word problem. Then exchange books with another student and solve their problem.

⑧   0   3   ②

I have 8 munee
I

Step In What words could you use to describe these vehicles?

We could use words like **big** and **small**, or **long** and **short**.
We could also describe the color, or the number of wheels.

Look at the 2D shapes below.

What facts do you know about each shape?

What words can you use to describe them?

1. Look at each shape. Write **true** or **false** for each fact.

Shape A 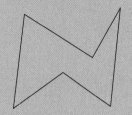	• It has five sides.	*false*
	• All sides are the same length.	*false*
	• All sides are straight.	*true*
Shape B 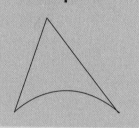	• It is a triangle.	*false*
	• It is a closed shape.	*true*
	• One side is curved.	*true*
Shape C 	• It has four corners.	*false*
	• It has straight parts.	*true*
	• It is a rectangle.	*false*

2. Draw two different shapes that match all the facts below.

• It has five sides.
• All sides are straight.
• One corner is very pointy.

Write one more true fact about these shapes in Question 1.

Shape A *it is closed Shape*

Shape B *It*

Think and Solve Imagine this shape pattern keeps going.

| 1 | 2 | 3 | 4 | 5 | 6 | 7 | 8 |

a. How many ☐ will be in the first 20 shapes? ☐

b. How many ◯ will be in the first 20 shapes? ☐

Words at Work Write the answer for each clue in the grid.
Use words from the list.

Clues Across

2. A non-square rectangles has four straight __ .

4. Five fish __ away one fish is four fish.

5. A triangle has __ straight sides.

Clues Down

1. You can __ back to subtract.

2. A circle is a 2D __ with no straight sides.

3. The sides of a square are all the __ in length.

three
same
count
take
sides
shape

© ORIGO Education

1. Color the **longest** pencil red.
   Color the **shortest** pencil blue.

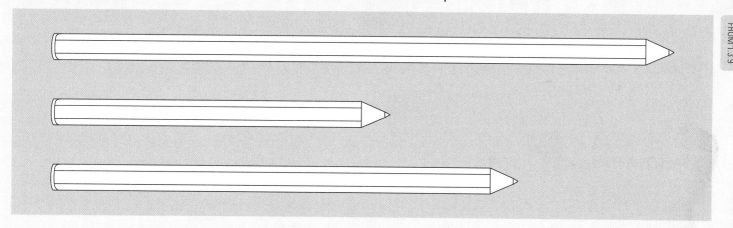

FROM 1.3.9

2. Solve each problem. Show your thinking.

a. José uses 9 blocks to make a car. Brianna only uses 7 blocks. How many more blocks does José use?

b. Carol buys a box of blocks for 8 dollars. Terek buys a box for 10 dollars. How much less does Carol spend?

FROM 1.4.6

☐ blocks

☐ dollars

Preparing for Module 5

Draw ◯ in the empty box to make the balance picture true. Then complete the sentence to match.

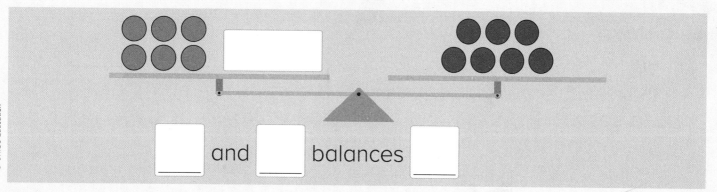

☐ and ☐ balances ☐

Step In   **In his kitchen, Jack sorts things into groups.**

He puts the spoons in one part of the drawer.

He puts the forks in another part of the drawer.

What are some things that get sorted into groups in your house?

Emma sorted these 2D shapes into two groups.
How did she figure out where they belong?

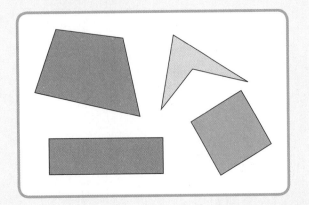 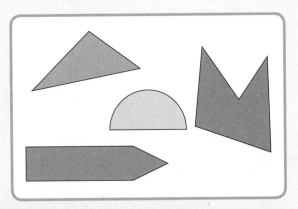

Step Up

Your teacher will give you some cards. Sort the cards into two groups and paste them into the two boxes on page 145. Then write a name for each group.

by the lins

Step Ahead   Circle two of these shapes.

Then write what is the same about them.

Step In What type of shape is this?

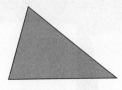

If we turn it around, does it become a different shape or stay the same shape?

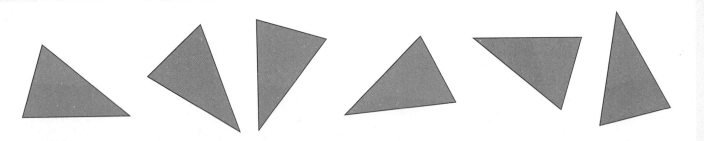

Step Up I. Look at the shapes below. Write **T** inside each triangle. Write **S** inside each square. Write **N** inside each non-square rectangle. Some shapes will not have a letter inside them.

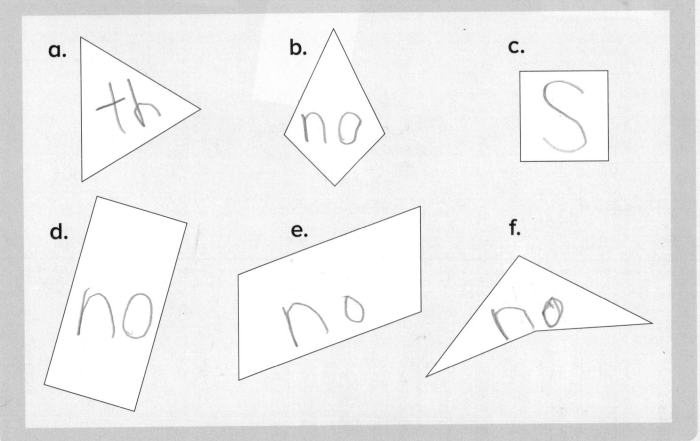

© ORIGO Education

2. Read the label inside each shape. Then use your ruler to
draw one or two straight sides to complete the shape.

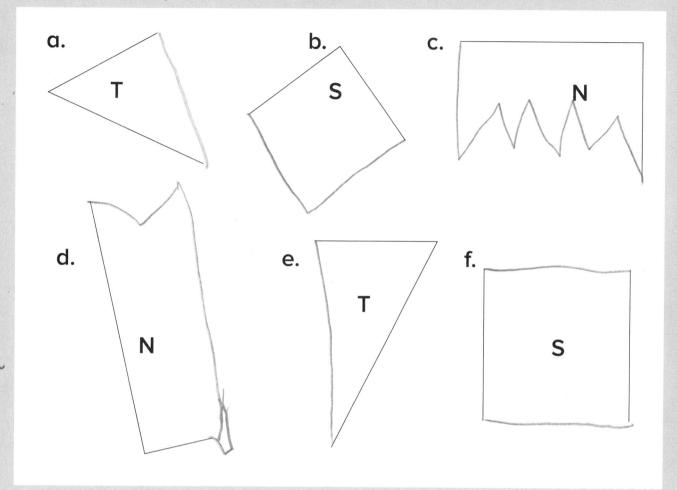

a. T

b. S

c. N

d. N

e. T

f. S

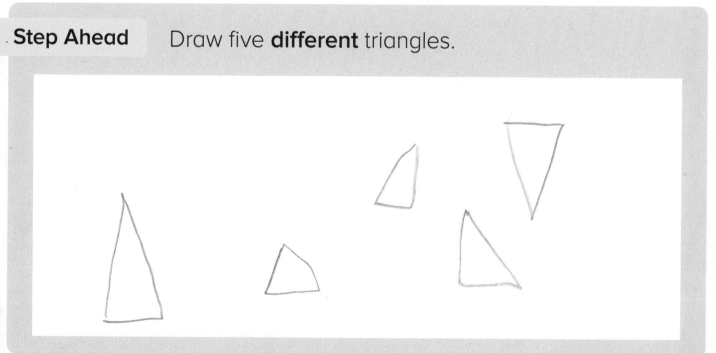

© ORIGO Education

Computation Practice   **Why did the hairdresser win the race?**

★ Complete the equations.

★ Write each letter above its matching total at the bottom of the page. Some letters are used more than once.

$6 = 3 + 3$ **k** $11 = 2 + 9$ **a**

$2 = 1 + 1$ **u** $9 = 1 + 8$ **r**

$4 = 2 + 2$ **e** $7 = 5 + 2$ **h**

$10 = 8 + 2$ **o** $3 = 2 + 1$ **c**

$8 = 4 + 4$ **s** $5 = 3 + 2$ **t**

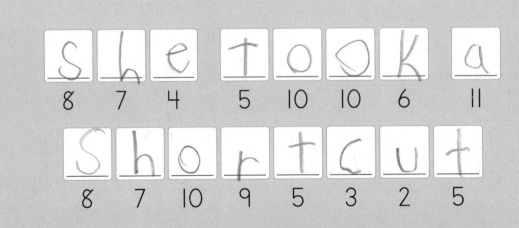

S	h	e		t	o	o	k		a
8	7	4		5	10	10	6		11

S	h	o	r	t	c	u	t
8	7	10	9	5	3	2	5

ORIGO Stepping Stones · Grade 1 · 4.10

© ORIGO Education

1. Color the pictures that are about the same length as the cube train.

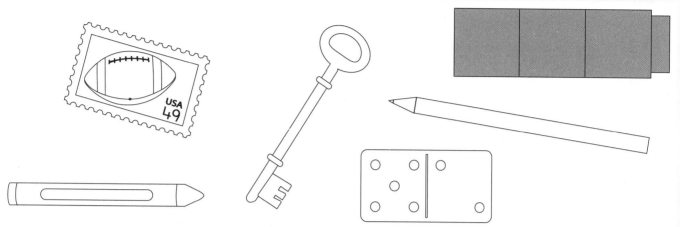

FROM 1.3.11

2. These shapes have been sorted into two groups.

   a. Write a label for each group to describe the sort.
   b. Draw one more shape in each group.

FROM 1 4.9

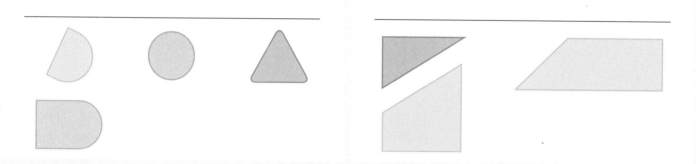

Write the numeral to match each group of dots. Then circle the group that has **fewer**.

a.

b.

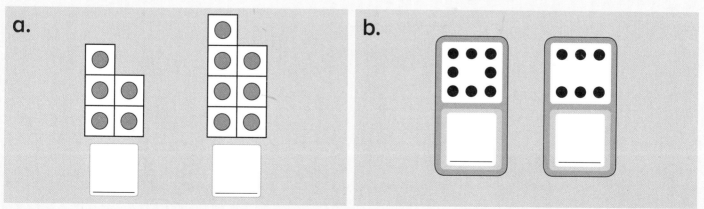

© ORIGO Education

Step In

Abigail starts to draw a shape.
This is what she draws.

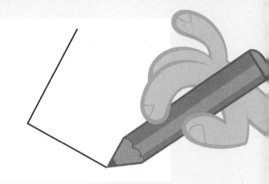

Which of these shapes could
Abigail be drawing?

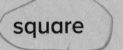

square

circle

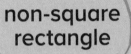

non-square
rectangle

hexagon

triangle

A **hexagon** is a closed shape
with six straight sides.

The shape has some straight
sides, so it won't be a circle.

Step Up   I.   Trace each shape. Then write the shape name.

a.
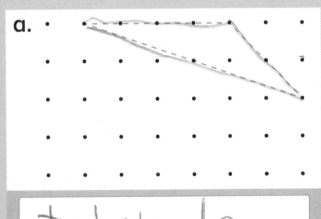

triangle

b.
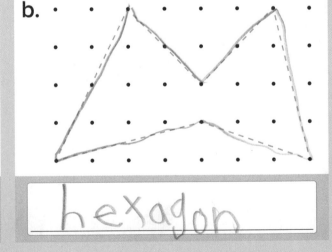

hexagon

2. Draw each shape.

a.   triangle

b.   square

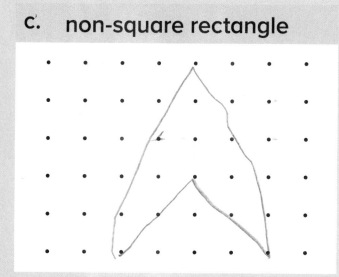

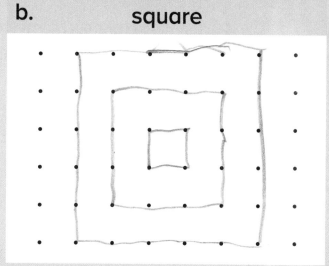

c.   non-square rectangle

d.   hexagon

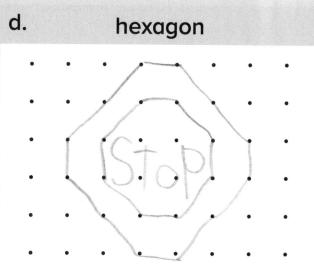

Step Ahead   Draw two hexagons that look different.

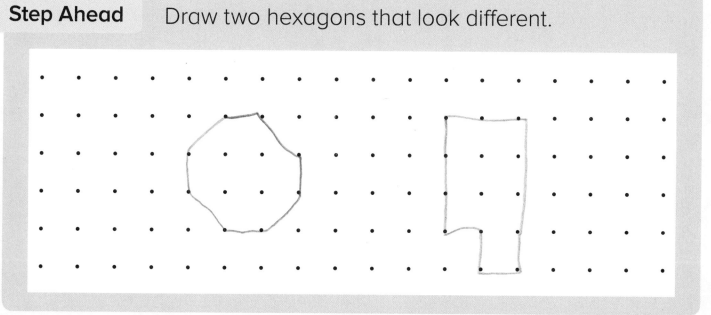

Step In

A new shape was made by tracing around these two pattern blocks.

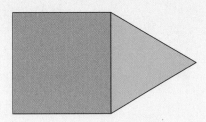

Which two shapes do you see?

How many sides does the new shape have?

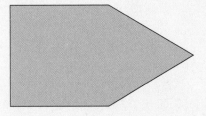

Step Up 1. Choose **two other** pattern blocks.

a. Join them together. Then trace around them below.

b. How many sides does your new shape have? _____

2. Choose **three** different pattern blocks.

a. Join them. Then trace around them.

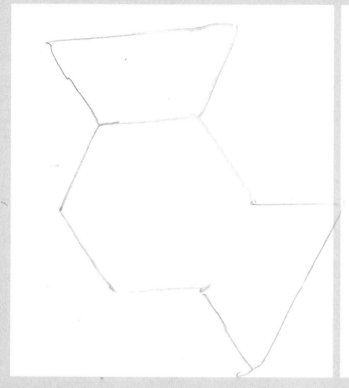

b. How many sides does your new shape have?

3. Choose **three** different pattern blocks.

a. Join them. Then trace around them.

b. How many sides does your new shape have?

Step Ahead

Each shape below was made using **three** pattern blocks. Draw lines on the shapes to show which blocks were used.

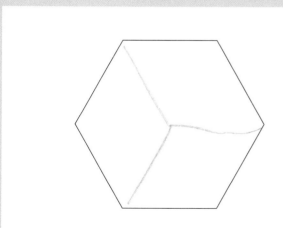
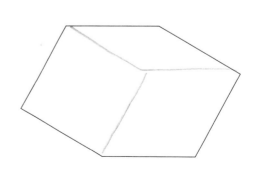

© ORIGO Education

Think and Solve Same shapes are the same number. Write the missing number to complete the equation.

$$\triangle + \triangle = 16 \qquad \square + \triangle = 10$$

$$\square + \square + \triangle = \boxed{}$$

Words at Work Circle one of these 2D shapes. Write about your 2D shape. Use words from the list to help.

  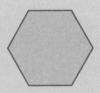

circle
hexagon
triangle
straight
curved
side

I. Color the crayon that is 4 ants long.

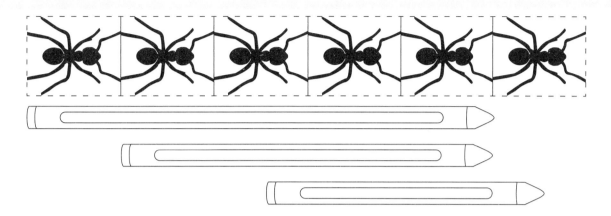

FROM 1.3.12

2. Write **T** inside each triangle. Write **S** inside each square. Write **N** inside each non-square rectangle.

a.    b. 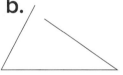   c.   d.

e.    f.    g.   h.

FROM 1.4.10

Preparing for Module 5   Color the number that is greater.

a.

b.

c.

d.

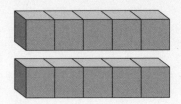

Step In   What doubles fact do these cubes show?

What equation can you write to show this double?

$$5 + 5 = 10$$

How can you use that doubles fact to figure out the total number of these cubes?

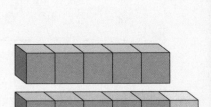

5 plus 6
is the same value as
double 5 and 1 more.
So 5 + 6 is 11.

What equation can you write to match this fact?

Step Up   I.   Write the answers.

a.
Double 4 is   8

b.
Double 9 is   18

c.
Double 6 is   12

d.
Double 5 is 10

e.
Double 3 is 6

f.
Double 7 is 14

g.
Double 10 is   20

h.
Double 8 is   16

2. Write the doubles fact. Draw **one more** dot on one end.
Then write the **double-plus-1** fact and its turnaround.

a.
$4 + 4 = 8$

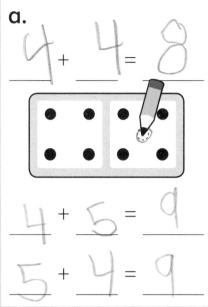

$4 + 5 = 9$

$5 + 4 = 9$

b.
$7 + 7 = 14$

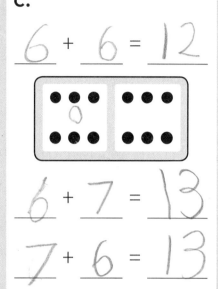

$7 + 8 = 15$

$8 + 7 = 15$

c.
$6 + 6 = 12$

$6 + 7 = 13$

$7 + 6 = 13$

d.
$3 + 3 = 6$

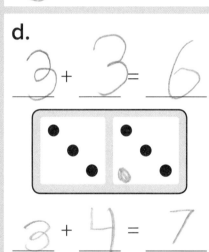

$3 + 4 = 7$

$4 + 3 = 7$

e.
$5 + 5 = 10$

$6 + 5 = 11$

$5 + 6 = 11$

f.
$8 + 8 = 16$

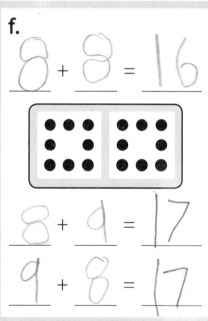

$8 + 9 = 17$

$9 + 8 = 17$

Step Ahead   Write the double you could use to help figure out each answer. Then write the total.

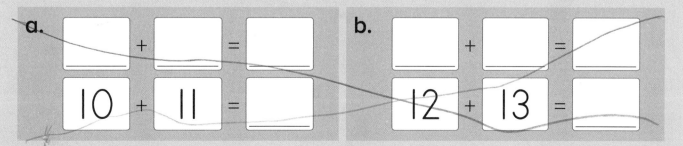

a.
☐ + ☐ = ☐

$10 + 11 = $ ☐

b.
☐ + ☐ = ☐

$12 + 13 = $ ☐

© ORIGO Education

Step In

Look at this part of a number track.

What equations can you complete that are doubles facts?

What numbers will you write?

How could you complete the equation that is not a double?

I would use a doubles fact to help me.

7	
8	= ☐ + ☐
9	= ☐ + ☐
10	= ☐ + ☐
11	

Step Up

I. Circle the dominoes that show a **double-plus-1** fact.

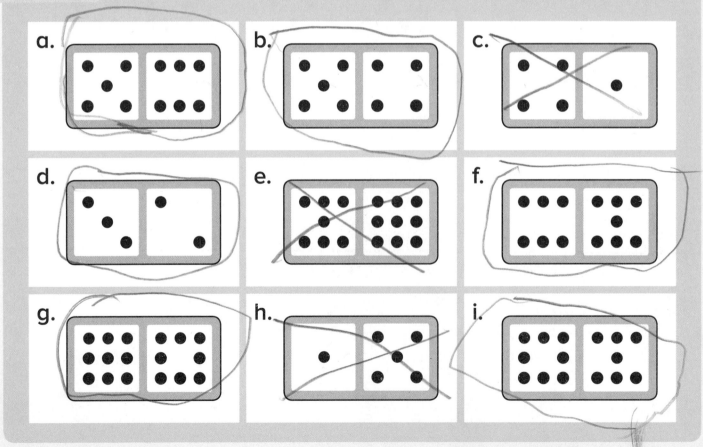

a.   b.   c.

d.   e.   f.

g.   h.   i.

© ORIGO Education

2. Write the doubles fact you can use to figure out the total number of dots on each domino. Then write the total for each **double-plus-1** fact.

a.

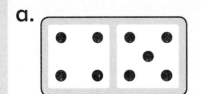

Double $\boxed{4}$ is $\boxed{8}$

SO

$4 + 5 = \boxed{9}$

b.

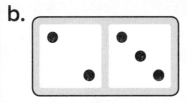

Double $\boxed{2}$ is $\boxed{2}$

SO

$2 + 3 = \boxed{5}$

c.

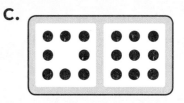

Double $\boxed{}$ is $\boxed{}$

SO

$8 + 9 = \boxed{}$

d.

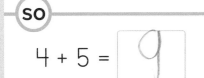

Double $\boxed{}$ is $\boxed{}$

SO

$3 + 4 = \boxed{}$

e.

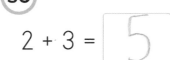

Double $\boxed{}$ is $\boxed{}$

SO

$7 + 6 = \boxed{}$

f.

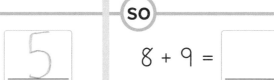

Double $\boxed{}$ is $\boxed{}$

SO

$6 + 5 = \boxed{}$

Step Ahead   Write count-on facts that are also doubles facts or double-plus-1 facts.

_____   _____

_____   _____

Computation Practice

★ Complete the equations as fast as you can.

start

$8 + 2 = 10$ $4 + 6 = 10$ $1 + 9 = 10$

$4 + 1 = 5$ $2 + 7 = 9$ $5 + 3 = 8$

$6 + 8 = 14$ $7 + 5 = 12$ $2 + 1 = 3$

$2 + 9 = 11$ $5 + 2 = 7$ $2 + 6 = 8$

$1 + 5 = 6$ $4 + 5 = 9$ $1 + 7 = 8$

$3 + 4 = 7$ $6 + 1 = 7$ $2 + 3 = 5$

$3 + 1 = 4$ $2 + 4 = 6$ **finish**

I. Write an equation to match each picture.

a.

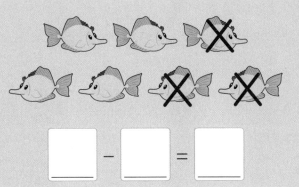

☐ − ☐ = ☐

b.

☐ − ☐ = ☐

FROM 1.4.1

2. Write the doubles fact. Draw **one more** dot on one end. Then write the double-plus-1 fact and its turnaround.

a.

☐ + ☐ = ☐

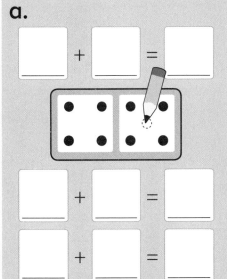

☐ + ☐ = ☐

☐ + ☐ = ☐

b.

☐ + ☐ = ☐

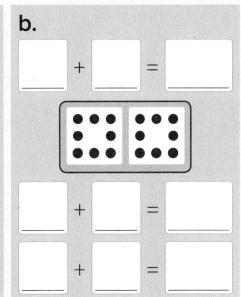

☐ + ☐ = ☐

☐ + ☐ = ☐

c.

☐ + ☐ = ☐

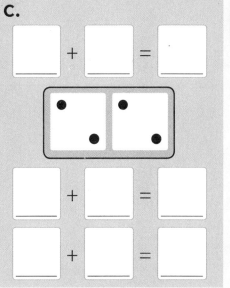

☐ + ☐ = ☐

☐ + ☐ = ☐

FROM 1.5.1

Preparing for Module 6   Write an equation to match each picture.

a.

☐ − ☐ = ☐

b.

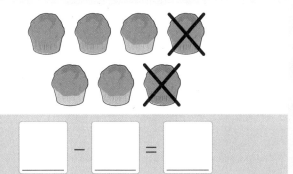

☐ − ☐ = ☐

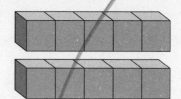

Step In **What doubles fact do these cubes show?**

What equation can you write to show this double?

[ ] + [ ] = [ ]

How can you use that doubles fact to figure out the total number of these cubes?

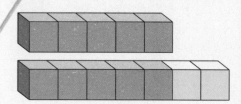

5 plus 7 is the same value as double 5 and 2 more. So 5 + 7 is 12.

What equation can you write to match this fact?

Step Up **I.** Write the answers.

a. Double 4 is [ ]   Double 4 plus 2 more is [ ]

b. Double 7 is [ ]   Double 7 plus 2 more is [ ]

c. Double 5 is [ ]   Double 5 plus 2 more is [ ]

d. Double 9 is [ ]   Double 9 plus 2 more is [ ]

e. Double 8 is [ ]   Double 8 plus 2 more is [ ]

2. Write the doubles fact. Draw **two more** dots on one end. Then write the **double-plus-2** fact and its turnaround.

a.
2 + 2 = 4

2 + 4 = 6
4 + 2 = 6

b.
4 + 4 = 8

4 + 6 = 10
6 + 4 = 10

c.
7 + 7 = 14

7 + 9 = 16
9 + 7 = 16

d.
5 + 5 = 10

5 + 7 = 12
7 + 5 = 12

e.
3 + 3 = 6

5 + 3 = 8
3 + 5 = 8

f.
6 + 6 = 12

8 + 6 = 14
6 + 8 = 14

Step Ahead   Write the numbers.

a. If you double me and add 2, the answer is 18.

What number am I? 16

b. If you double me and add 2, the answer is 22.

What number am I? 20

Step In Look at these numbers.

| 5 | (8) | 14 | 11 | 6 | 15 |

Which number is equal to double 4?

Which number is the sum of 3 and 5?

What do you notice?

> The **sum** is the total in an addition equation. For example, 12 is the sum of 7 + 5.

Which numbers will you get if you use doubling? How do you know?

Which numbers will you get if you double and add 1?

Which numbers will you get if you double and add 2?

Step Up 1. Circle the dominoes that show a **double-plus-2** fact.

a.
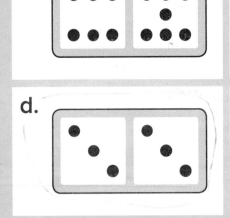

b.

c.
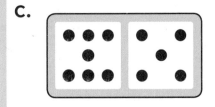

d.

e.
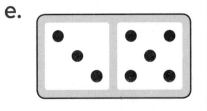

f.
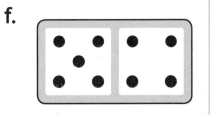

g.
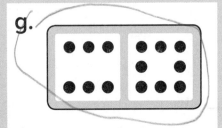

h.

i.
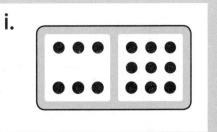

2. Write the doubles fact you can use to figure out the total on each domino. Then write the total for each **double-plus-2** fact.

a.

Double [4] is [4]

so

5 + 3 = [8]

b.

Double [5] is [5]

so

6 + 4 = [10]

c.

Double [8] is [8]

so

7 + 9 = [16]

d.
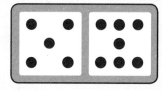

Double [6] is [6]

so

5 + 7 = [12]

e.

Double [7] is [7]

so

8 + 6 = [14]

Step Ahead

Akari has 6 dollars. Her mom gives her 8 dollars more to buy a toy. Circle each toy that Akari can buy with the total money.

10 dollars

18 dollars

11 dollars

13 dollars

15 dollars

12 dollars

Think and Solve Imagine you toss two beanbags and they both land on the target.

a. What is the **greatest** (biggest) total you can get?

b. What is the **least** (smallest) total?

c. What other totals can you get?

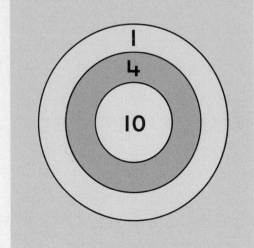

Words at Work

a. Write a double-plus-1 word problem. You can use words from the list to help.

| plus |
| double |
| same |
| add |
| total |
| dollars |
| cost |

b. Write an equation to match your word problem.

☐ + ☐ = ☐

1. Complete the equation to match each picture.

a.

$\boxed{4} - \boxed{2} = \boxed{2}$

b.

$\boxed{6} - \boxed{2} = \boxed{4}$

FROM 1.4.2

2. Write the doubles fact you can use to figure out the total on each domino. Then write the total for each **double-plus-1** fact.

FROM 1.5.2

a.

Double $\boxed{4}$ is $\boxed{5}$

so

$4 + 5 = \boxed{}$

b.

Double $\boxed{}$ is $\boxed{}$

so

$3 + 4 = \boxed{}$

c.

Double $\boxed{}$ is $\boxed{}$

so

$6 + 7 = \boxed{}$

Count on 1 or 2 pennies. Then write the equation to match.

a.

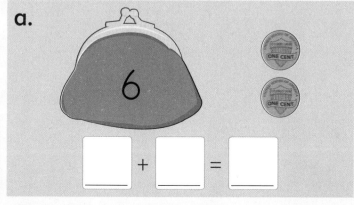

$\boxed{} + \boxed{} = \boxed{}$

b.

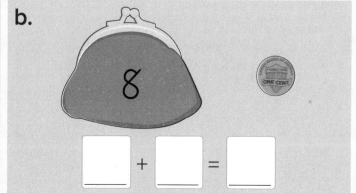

$\boxed{} + \boxed{} = \boxed{}$

Step In Look at these toys and prices.

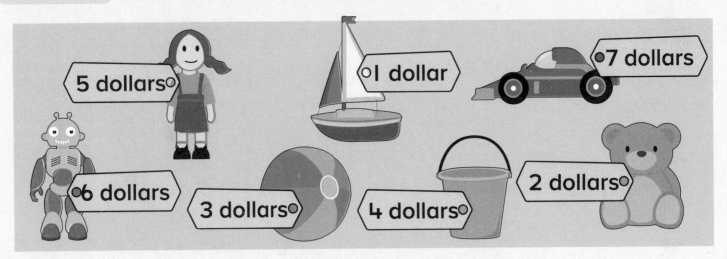

How can you figure out the total cost of the bucket and doll?

How can you figure out the total cost of the ball and bear?
What other way could you figure it out?

What other totals can you figure out using that strategy?

Step Up 1. Look at the toys and prices above.
Write an equation to show the total cost.

a.

$6 + 5 = 11$ dollars

b.
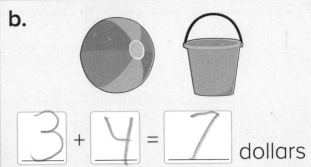

$3 + 4 = 7$ dollars

c.
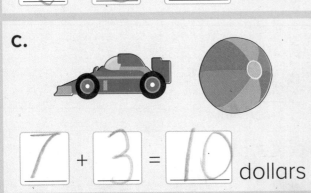

$7 + 3 = 10$ dollars

d.

$5 + 2 = 7$ dollars

2. Find the toys and prices at the top of page 170.
Write an equation to show the total cost.

a.

$4 + 2 = 6$ dollars

b.

$7 + 6 = 12$ dollars

c.

$5 + 3 = 8$ dollars

d.

$7 + 5 = 12$ dollars

e.

$1 + 2 = 3$ dollars

f.

$6 + 4 = 10$ dollars

Step Ahead   Write **true** or **false** for each sentence.

a. Counting on is one way to figure out the total cost for the **doll** and the **bear**.

b. You can double-add-1 to figure out the total cost of the **doll** and the **bucket**.

c. The price of the **robot** plus the price of the **ball** is a doubles fact.

| Step In | What two numbers are shown on this pan balance? |

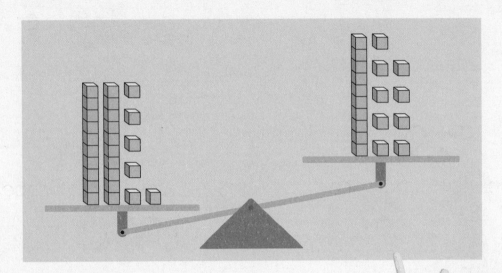

Why don't the two numbers balance?

Which number is greater? How do you know?

The greater number must be heavier.

How could you add more blocks to make the two numbers balance?

| Step Up | I. | Write numbers to match the blocks. Then circle the **greater** number. |

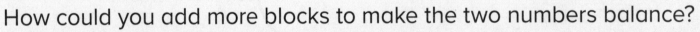

a.

42 does not balance 38

b.

53 does not balance 61

2. Write numbers to match the blocks.
Then circle the number that is **less**.

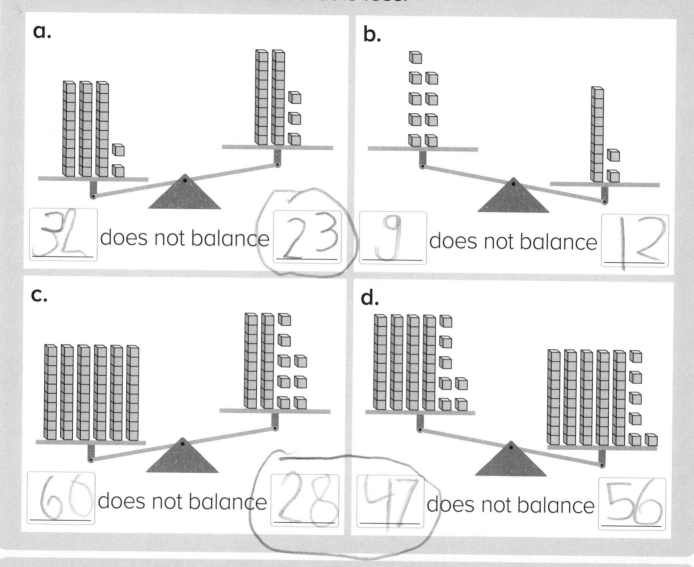

a. 32 does not balance (23)

b. 9 does not balance 12

c. 60 does not balance (28

d. 47) does not balance 56

Step Ahead Draw more blocks to make these balance pictures true. Then write the numbers.

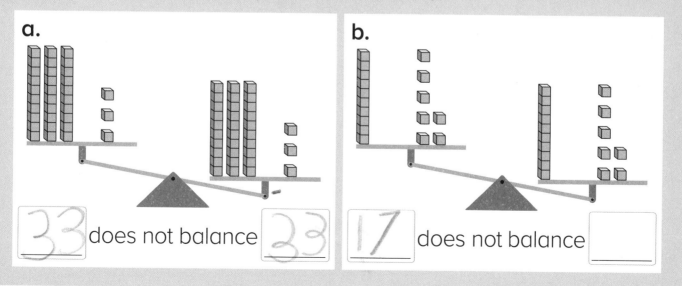

a. 33 does not balance 33

b. 17 does not balance

© ORIGO Education

Computation Practice

★ Write the totals for each pair of facts.

★ Draw a line to the fingerprint that matches the total in each magnifying glass.

★ Circle the fingerprint that has no match.

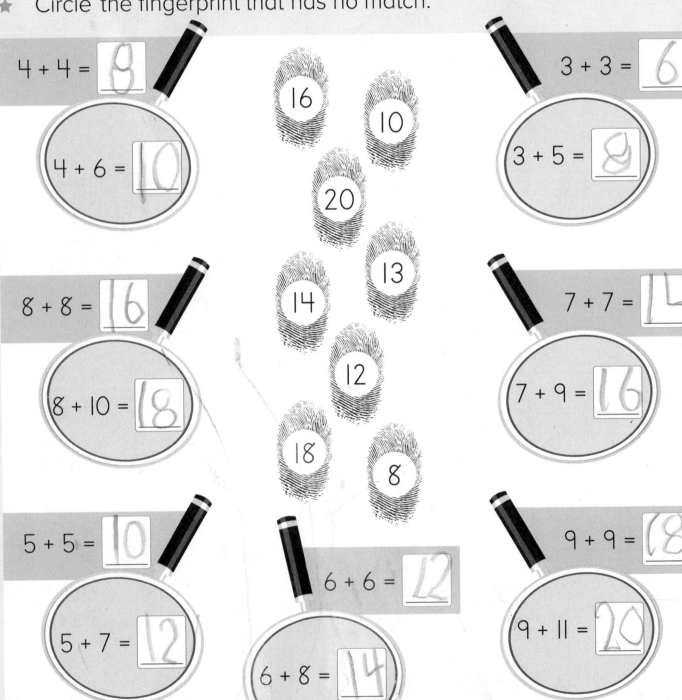

4 + 4 = 8

4 + 6 = 10

3 + 3 = 6

3 + 5 = 8

8 + 8 = 16

8 + 10 = 18

7 + 7 = 14

7 + 9 = 16

5 + 5 = 10

5 + 7 = 12

6 + 6 = 12

6 + 8 = 14

9 + 9 = 18

9 + 11 = 20

16   10   20   13   14   12   18   8

Ongoing Practice

1. Write an equation to show the blocks that are left in the container.

a.  Take out **1**.

5 blocks $5 - 1 = 4$

b.  Take out **2**.

8 blocks $8 - 2 = 6$

c.  Take out **2**.

6 blocks $6 - 2 = 4$

d. 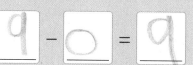 Take out **0**.

9 blocks $9 - 0 = 9$

2. Write the doubles fact you can use to figure out the total on each domino. Then write the total for each **double-plus-2** fact.

a.

Double ☐ is ☐

SO

$7 + 5 = $ ☐

b.

Double ☐ is ☐

SO

$4 + 6 = $ ☐

c.

Double ☐ is ☐

SO

$9 + 7 = $ ☐

Preparing for Module 6

Draw the same number of dots on the other wing. Then write the numbers.

a.

☐ + ☐ = ☐

double ☐ = ☐

b.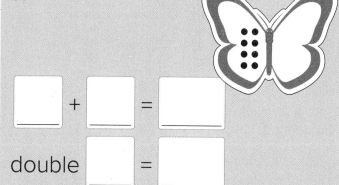

☐ + ☐ = ☐

double ☐ = ☐

Step In   How many tens blocks are yellow?

How many ones blocks are yellow?
How many tens and ones blocks are purple?

Which color shows the greater number?
How do you know?

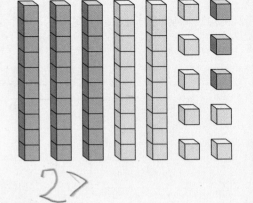

I looked at the tens first.
There are 3 purple tens
and only 2 yellow tens.

Step Up   1.   Color blocks to match each number name.
Then write the numbers to complete the statement.

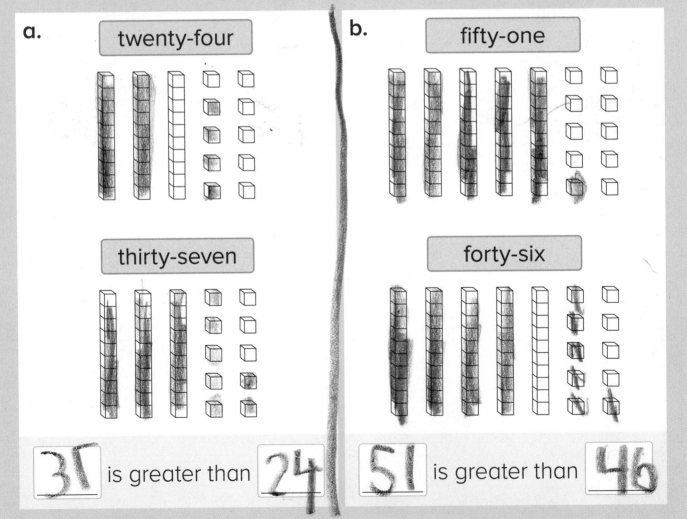

a.

twenty-four

thirty-seven

37 is greater than 24

b.

fifty-one

forty-six

51 is greater than 46

2. Color blocks to match each number name.
Then write the numbers to complete the statement.

a.

thirteen

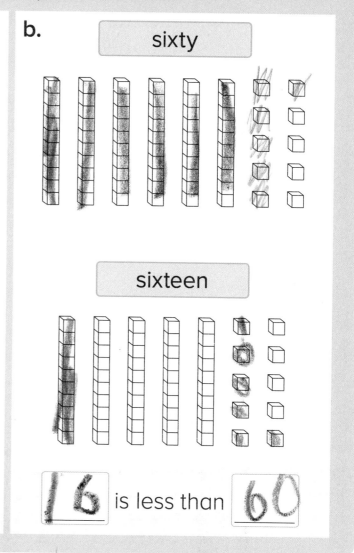

thirty-three

_13_ is less than _33_

b.

sixty

sixteen

_16_ is less than _60_

Step Ahead   Which way is house number 59?
Draw an arrow on the street to show the direction.

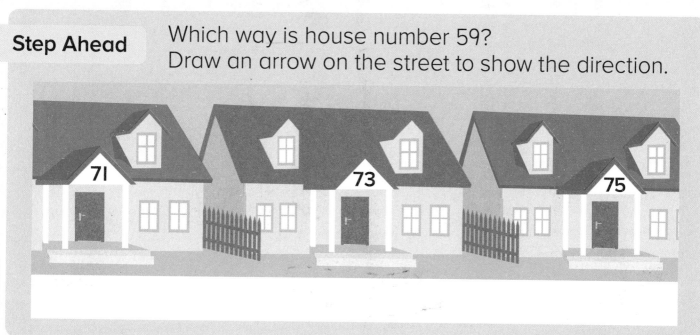

71   73   75

© ORIGO Education

Step In

Compare the number of tens and ones in each place-value chart.

Tens	Ones
5	1

Tens	Ones
3	8

Is 51 **greater than** or **less than** 38?
How do you know?

When comparing two numbers, which place do you look at first?

What would you do if the digits in the tens place were the same?

Step Up

1. Compare the numbers in the charts.
   Circle the words that are true.

a.

Tens	Ones
7	5

(is greater than)

is less than

Tens	Ones
5	2

b.

Tens	Ones
4	6

is greater than

(is less than)

Tens	Ones
5	0

c.

Tens	Ones
2	9

(is greater than)

is less than

Tens	Ones
2	2

d.

Tens	Ones
3	8

is greater than

(is less than)

Tens	Ones
6	8

2. Compare the numbers. Write **is greater than** or **is less than** to make true statements.

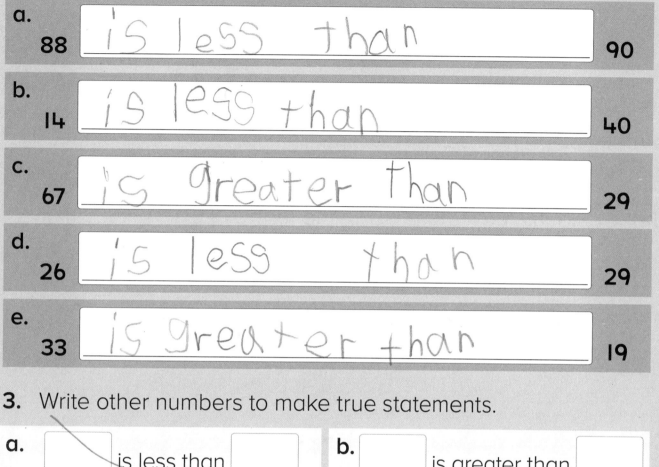

a. 88 ___is less than___ 90

b. 14 ___is less than___ 40

c. 67 ___is greater than___ 29

d. 26 ___is less than___ 29

e. 33 ___is greater than___ 19

3. Write other numbers to make true statements.

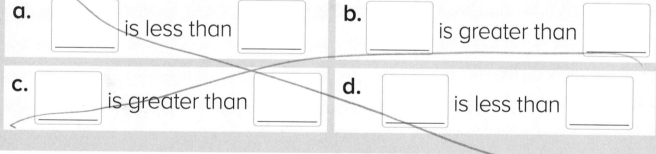

a. [ ] is less than [ ]

b. [ ] is greater than [ ]

c. [ ] is greater than [ ]

d. [ ] is less than [ ]

Step Ahead Write the digits in the boxes to make true statements. Use each digit only once.

0	1	2	3
4	5	6	7
8	8	9	9

[ ][ ] is less than [ ][ ]

[ ][ ] is greater than [ ][ ]

[ ][ ] is less than [ ][ ]

Think and Solve

Della is 2 years older than Cara.
Anya is one year younger than Della.
Cara is 5 years old.

How old is Anya? ☐

Words at Work

Choose and write a word from the list to complete each sentence below. Some words are used more than once.

> thirty
> fifty-five
> tens
> greater
> less
> ones

a. _____ does not balance eleven.

b. Thirteen is _____ than twelve.

c. Seventeen is _____ than eighteen,
   but _____ than sixteen.

d. Forty-four is _____ than forty-one
   because it has three more _____ .

e. _____ is greater than thirty-five
   because it has two more _____ .

Ongoing Practice

1. Solve each problem. Draw pictures or write equations to show your thinking.

FROM 1.4.7

a. Isaac buys a vase for 8 dollars and flowers for 5 dollars. How much does he spend?

b. Ava buys a book for 6 dollars. She pays with a 10-dollar bill. How much will she get back?

☐ dollars

☐ dollars

2. Write the totals. Then write **C** or **D** in the circles to show the strategy you used to figure out each total.

FROM 1.5.5

Addition strategy

Ⓒ count-on

Ⓓ doubles

○ 7 + 1 = ☐

○ 2 + 6 = ☐

○ 3 + 4 = ☐

○ 4 + 5 = ☐

○ 5 + 6 = ☐

○ 5 + 5 = ☐

○ 1 + 5 = ☐

○ 7 + 5 = ☐

Preparing for Module 6

Color each glass to match its label.

a.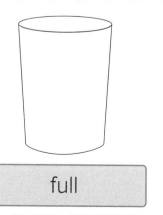

full

b.

half full

c.

empty

Step In   What does this picture show?

PLAYER	SCORE
COLE	92
LUIS	51
DONNA	55
ISABELLE	78

How could you order these scores from **least** to **greatest**?

Step Up   I.   Write these numbers in order from **least** to **greatest**.

a.

| 22 | 15 | 28 | 31 |

15 22 28 31

b.

| 54 | 63 | 45 | 72 |

45 54 63 72

c.

| 18 | 33 | 41 | 39 |

18 33 39 41

d.

| 78 | 71 | 69 | 80 |

69 71 78 86

2. Write these numbers in order from **greatest** to **least**.

a.
| 29 | 31 | 24 | 19 |

31 29 24 19

b.
| 48 | 42 | 46 | 55 |

____ ____ ____ ____

c.
| 65 | 70 | 73 | 61 |

____ ____ ____ ____

d.
| 90 | 82 | 88 | 18 |

____ ____ ____ ____

3. Write numbers to show **least** to **greatest**.

| 13 | 17 | 27 | ____ | ____ | 52 |

4. Write numbers to show **greatest** to **least**.

| 88 | ____ | 61 | 36 | ____ | 4 |

Step Ahead   Read the story. Then write each name above the score that matches.

a. **Giselle's** score is greater than **Wendell's** score.
Luke's score is less than **Wendell's**.

_____   _____   _____
| 13 | | 22 | | 34 |

b. **Dena's** score is greater than **Logan's** but less than **Richard's**.

_____   _____   _____
| 35 | | 42 | | 57 |

Step In Look at this block picture.

Which side has the greater
number of blocks?

**Look at the comparison sentence
below the picture.**
How does it match the picture?

What do you think > means?

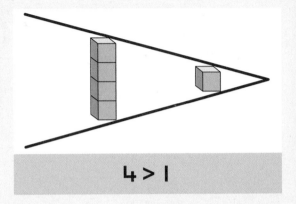

4 > 1

ⓘ When read from left to right, the symbol > means **is greater than.**

Look at this block picture.
Which side has the **greater**
number of blocks?

**Look at the comparison sentence
below the picture.**
How does it match the picture?

What do you think < means?

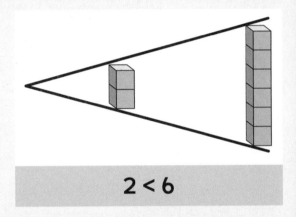

2 < 6

ⓘ When read from left to right, the symbol < means **is less than.**

Step Up 1. Compare each stack.
Then write **<** or **>** to complete each sentence.

a.

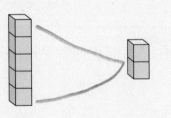

5   2

b.

3   6

2. Write the numbers and **<** or **>** to complete each sentence.

a.
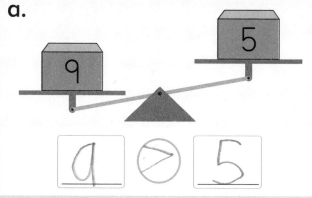

9 ⟩ 5

b.
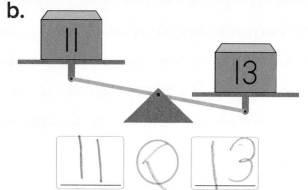

11 ◯ 13

c.
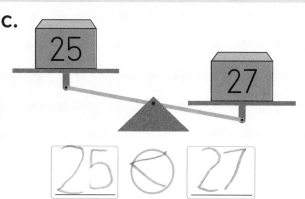

25 ◯ 27

d.
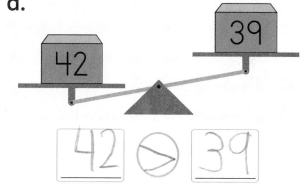

42 ◯ 39

3. Circle the sentences that are true.

a. (19 > 16)   b. 34 < 29   c. (8 < 10)   d. 17 > 71

Step Ahead   Use these numbers to make two true balance pictures. Then write comparison sentences to match.

| 13 | 10 | 15 | 12 |

a.
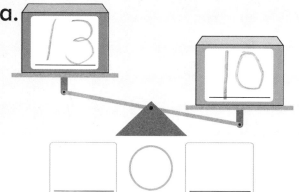

◯

b.
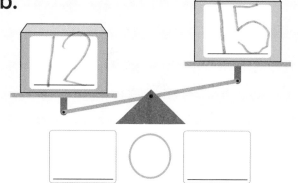

◯

Computation Practice **Who is hiding?**

★ Complete all the equations.

★ Find each total in the puzzle below and color it to match.

$8 + 9 = 17$	yellow	
$2 + 3 = 5$	purple	
$7 + 6 = 13$	blue	
$5 + 4 = 9$	green	

$6 + 5 = 11$	red	
$3 + 4 = 7$	orange	
$7 + 8 = 16$	pink	

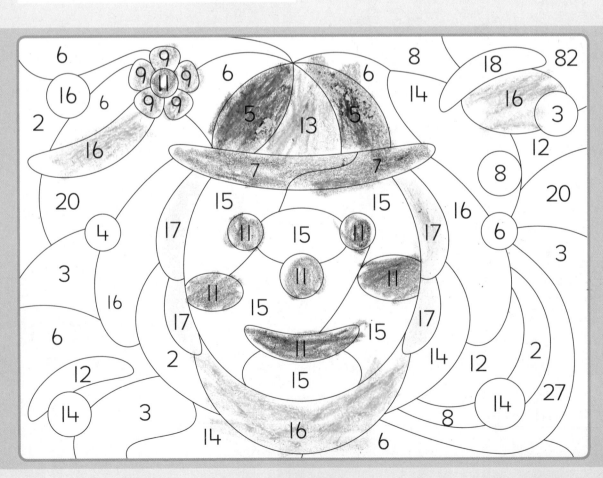

© ORIGO Education

Ongoing Practice

1. Look at the shape.
Write **true** or **false** for each fact.

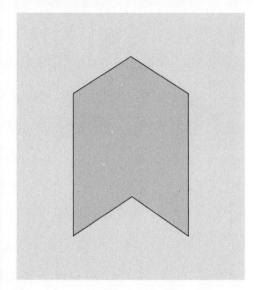

a. It is a closed shape.   _____

b. It has 6 corners.   _____

c. It has 5 sides.   _____

d. All sides are the same.   _____

2. Write numbers to match the blocks.
Then circle the number that is **less**.

a.

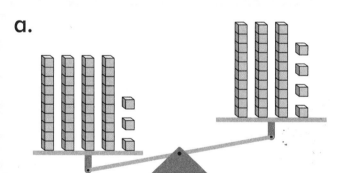

	does not balance	

b.

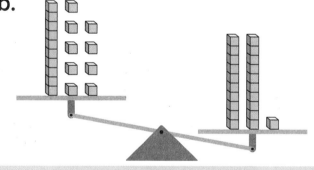

	does not balance	

Preparing for Module 6   Circle the egg carton that is half full.

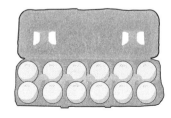

Step In Look at this balance picture.

What number could you write in the empty box on the left side? How do you know?

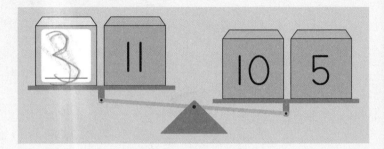

You could write any number less than 4 in the empty box.

What comparison sentence could you write?

Look at this balance picture.

What do you know about the numbers on the left side?

What numbers could you write?

Step Up

1. Write a number to make the balance picture true. Then write a comparison sentence using < or > to match.

a.

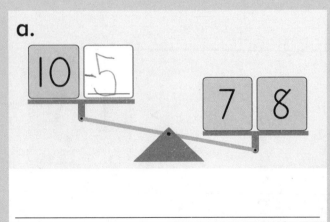

b.

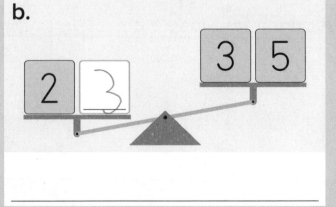

2. Write numbers to make the balance picture true.
Then write the comparison sentence to match.

a.
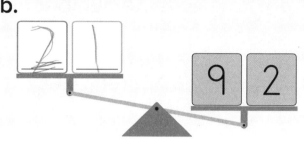
_____

b.
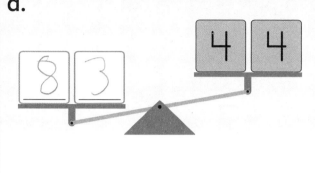
_____

c.
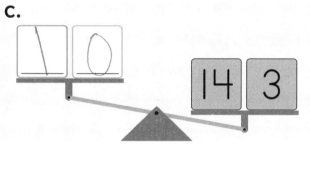
_____

d.
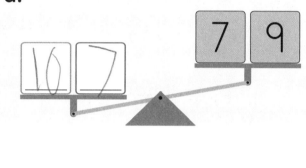
_____

3. Write **<**, **>**, or **=** to make true comparison sentences.

a.
14 + 3 ◯ 16 + 2

b.
6 + 7 ◯ 1 + 15

c.
5 + 7 ◯ 1 + 11

d.
8 + 9 ◯ 7 + 8

e.
19 + 0 ◯ 2 + 17

f.
2 + 13 ◯ 8 + 6

Step Ahead   Write the number to make true comparison sentences.

a.
$5 + 2 = 6 + 1$

b.
$6 + 4 > 4 + 5$

c.
$6 + 3 = 4 + 5$

d.
$10 + 1 < 7 + 5$

Step In   Read the number on each place-value chart.

Tens	Ones
4	9

Tens	Ones
7	0

How could you figure out which number is greater?

Complete this sentence to describe the two numbers.

70 > 49

What other sentence could you write to describe the two numbers?

49 < 70

Step Up   I.   Color blocks to match each number name.
Then write the numbers to complete the statement.

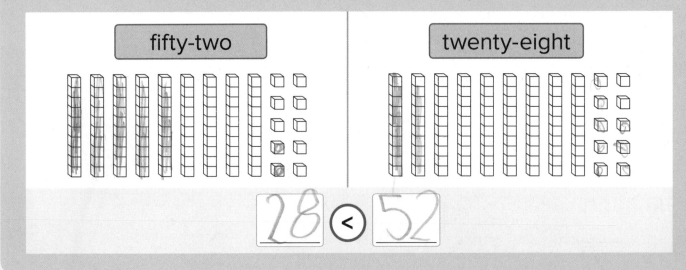

fifty-two   twenty-eight

28 < 52

2. Compare the numbers in the charts.
   Then write **<** or **>** to make a true statement.

a.

Tens	Ones
3	9

Tens	Ones
4	5

b.

Tens	Ones
8	2

Tens	Ones
6	4

c.

Tens	Ones
8	7

Tens	Ones
8	1

d.

Tens	Ones
9	1

Tens	Ones
1	9

3. Write **<** or **>** to compare these numbers.

a. 67 ⊘ 38   b. 95 ◯ 97   c. 7 ◯ 74

d. 35 ⊘ 18   e. 62 ◯ 68   f. 14 ◯ 41

Step Ahead   Write other numbers to make true statements.

a. 92 ⊙> 5   b. 30 ⊙< 100

c. 1 ⊙< 47   d. 5 ⊙> 2

Think and Solve

You can only move ⟶ or ↑.

⟶ is 1 unit.

How many units are in the **longest** path from **A** to **B**? ☐ units

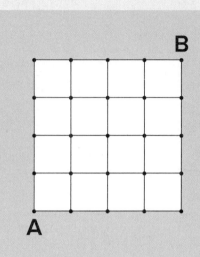

Words at Work

Imagine your friend was away from school when you learned about the symbols **<** and **>**.

Write about what the symbols mean and how they can be used. You can use words from the list to help you.

| greater than |
| points to |
| less than |
| open end |
| compare |
| numbers |
| tens |
| ones |

I. Draw each shape.

a. hexagon	b. triangle	c. non-square rectangle

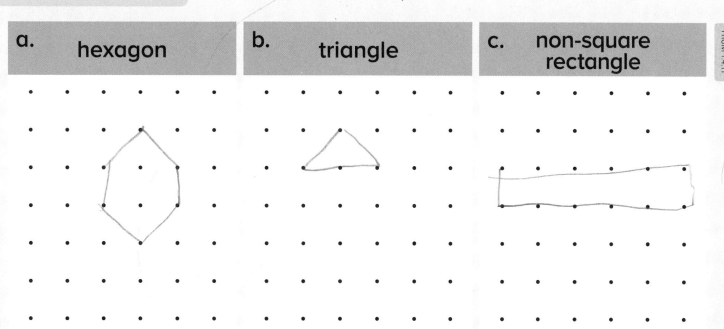

FROM 1.4.11

2. Write **<** or **>** to complete each balance statement.

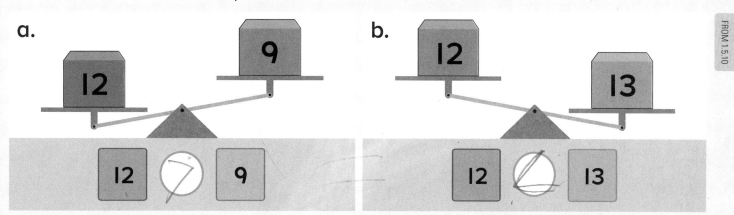

a.

12   $>$ 9

b.

12   $<$ 13

FROM 1.5.10

Circle the sandwich that has been cut in half.

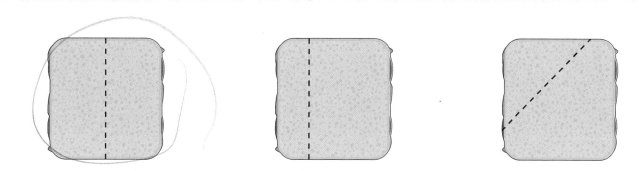

© ORIGO Education

Step In **Look at this picture.**

What addition story could you say about the picture?

Which number is the **total** in your story?

Which numbers are **parts** of the total?

What subtraction story could you say about the picture?

Which number is the **total** in your story?

Which numbers are **parts** of the total?

Step Up **I.** Write the number in each part and the total.

a.

One part is ____ .

The other part is ____ .

The total is ____ .

b.

One part is ____ .

The other part is ____ .

The total is ____ .

2. Complete each of these.

a.

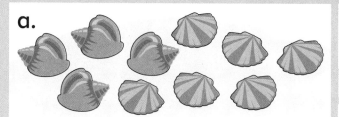

One part is _____.

The other part is _____.

The total is _____.

b.

One part is _____.

The other part is _____.

The total is _____.

c.

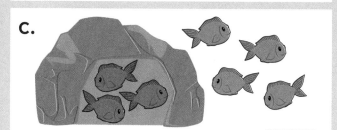

One part is _____.

The other part is _____.

The total is _____.

d.

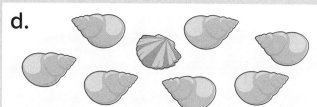

One part is _____.

The other part is _____.

The total is _____.

Step Ahead

Draw a picture to match the clues.

One part is 5.

The other part is 3.

The total is 8.

Step In   There were 8 muffins in this tray.

Some of the muffins were eaten.
How many muffins were eaten?
How do you know?

What is the total? What are the parts?

Step Up   1.   Draw more dots to match the total.
Then write the two parts.

a.   7 dots in all

6   1

b.   5 dots in all

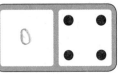

1   4

c.   6 dots in all

3   3

d.   7 dots in all

2   5

e.   4 dots in all

3   1

f.   5 dots in all

2   5

2. Draw more dots to match the total.
Then complete the addition fact.

a. 6 dots in all

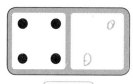

$4 + \boxed{2} = 6$

b. 7 dots in all

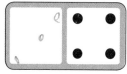

$\boxed{3} + 4 = 7$

c. 9 dots in all

$7 + \boxed{2} = 9$

d. 5 dots in all

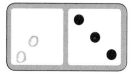

$\boxed{2} + 3 = 5$

e. 4 dots in all

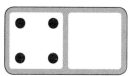

$4 + \boxed{0} = 4$

f. 8 dots in all

$5 + \boxed{3} = 8$

| **Step Ahead** | Read the problem. Write an addition fact that helps you figure out the answer. Then write the answer. |

a. Marcos has 7 toy cars. His brother gives him some more. Marcos now has 9 cars. How many cars did his brother give him?

$\boxed{7} + \boxed{2} = \boxed{9}$

$\boxed{9}$ cars

b. Deana has caught 9 fish. Then she catches some more. Now Deana has 12 fish. How many more fish did she catch?

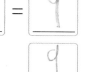

$\boxed{9} + \boxed{3} = \boxed{12}$

$\boxed{12}$ fish

Computation Practice

★ Complete the equations for each pair of facts.

$1 + 1 = \boxed{2}$ ➤ $1 + 2 = \boxed{3}$

$4 + 4 = \boxed{8}$ ➤ $4 + 5 = \boxed{9}$

$2 + 2 = \boxed{4}$ ➤ $2 + 3 = \boxed{5}$

$7 + 7 = \boxed{14}$ ➤ $7 + 8 = \boxed{15}$

$5 + 5 = \boxed{10}$ ➤ $5 + 6 = \boxed{11}$

$9 + 9 = \boxed{18}$ ➤ $9 + 10 = \boxed{19}$

$3 + 3 = \boxed{6}$ ➤ $3 + 4 = \boxed{7}$

$8 + 8 = \boxed{16}$ ➤ $8 + 9 = \boxed{17}$

$6 + 6 = \boxed{12}$ ➤ $6 + 7 = \boxed{13}$

Ongoing Practice

1. Write the doubles fact. Draw **one more** dot on one end. Then write the **double-plus-1** fact and its turnaround.

FROM 1.5.1

a.

[ ] + [ ] = [ ]

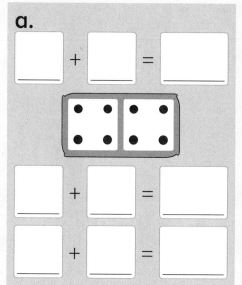

[ ] + [ ] = [ ]

[ ] + [ ] = [ ]

b.

[ ] + [ ] = [ ]

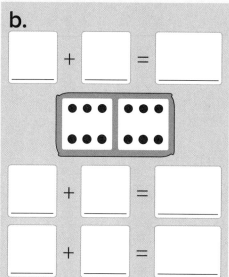

[ ] + [ ] = [ ]

[ ] + [ ] = [ ]

c.

[ ] + [ ] = [ ]

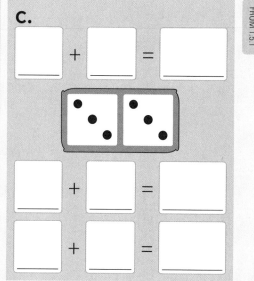

[ ] + [ ] = [ ]

[ ] + [ ] = [ ]

2. Write the number in each part and the total.

FROM 1.6.1

One part is _____ [ ].

The other part is _____ [ ].

The total is _____ [ ].

Preparing for Module 7 Write the number of tens and ones.

a.

[ ] tens [ ] ones

b.

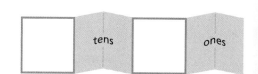

[ ] tens [ ] ones

ORIGO Stepping Stones · Grade 1 · 6.2

Step In

This card shows **two parts** and a **total**.

What do the numbers tell you?

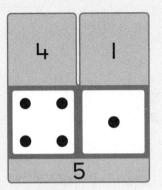

This card has one part hidden.

How can you use addition to help you figure out the part that is hidden?

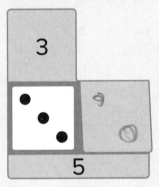

I know the total is 5, and one part is 3. I also know 3 and 2 is 5, so the missing part must be 2.

Step Up

1. Write the missing number and draw the matching dots on each card. Then complete the addition facts.

a.

6 + 2 = 8

b.

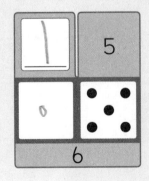

1 + 5 = 6

c.

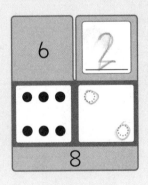

7 + 2 = 9

2. Complete the addition fact for each card.

a.

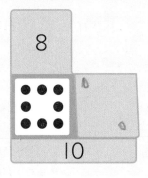

$8 + \boxed{2} = 10$

b.

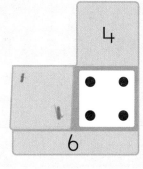

$\boxed{2} + 4 = 6$

c.

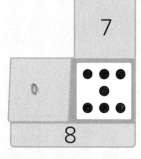

$\boxed{1} + 7 = 8$

d.

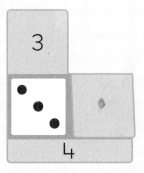

$3 + \boxed{1} = 4$

e.

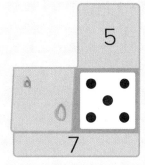

$\boxed{2} + 5 = 7$

f.

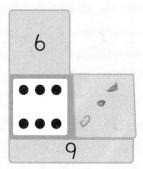

$6 + \boxed{3} = 9$

3. Write the missing number to complete each addition fact.

a. $\boxed{1} + 6 = 7$

b. $4 + \boxed{2} = 6$

c. $7 + \boxed{2} = 9$

Step Ahead	Write an addition fact that helps you figure out the answer. Then write the answer.

There are 9 birds on a fence.
Some birds fly away.
There are now 6 birds
sitting on the fence.
How many birds flew away?

$\boxed{6} + \boxed{3} = \boxed{9}$

$\boxed{9}$ birds

© ORIGO Education

Step In

There are 10 carrots growing in the ground. Some are taken during the night.

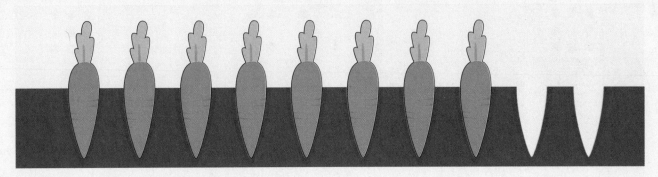

How many carrots have been taken? How do you know?

What is the total? What are the parts?

Complete this addition fact to figure out the carrots that have been taken.

$8 + \boxed{2} = 10$

Complete this subtraction fact to figure out the carrots that have been taken.

$10 - 8 = \boxed{2}$

Did you find it easier to use addition or subtraction to solve this problem?

Step Up

1. Complete the addition fact to figure out the carrots that were taken. Then complete the subtraction fact.

a.
$7 + \boxed{1} = 8$

$8 - 7 = \boxed{1}$

b.
$6 + \boxed{3} = 9$

$9 - 6 = \boxed{3}$

2. Figure out the number of dots that are covered.
Then complete the facts.

a. 5 − 3 = 2

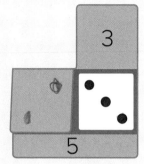

3

5

3 + 2 = 5

b. 9 − 7 = 2

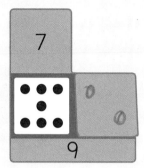

7

9

7 + 2 = 9

c. 6 − 5 = 1

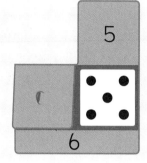

5

6

5 + 1 = 6

d. 8 − 5 = 3

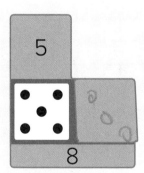

5

8

5 + 3 = 8

e. 4 − 3 = 1

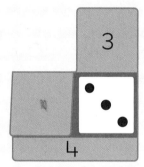

3

4

3 + 1 = 4

f. 7 − 4 = 3

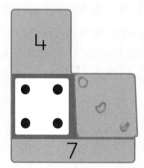

4

7

4 + 3 = 7

Step Ahead Solve this problem.
Show your thinking.

There are 9 berries in a packet.
4 berries are eaten on Monday.
3 berries are eaten on Tuesday.
How many berries are left?

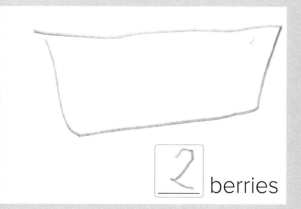

2 berries

Think and Solve

Michael is one year younger than Lindsay. Joel is 3 years older than Lindsay. Michael is 5 years old.

How old is Joel? ☐

Words at Work

Write the answer for each clue in the grid.
Use words from the list.

Clues Across

1. Take away means __.
4. Nine take away __ is eight.
5. Twelve less three is __.
6. The answer in a subtraction problem is the unknown __.

Clues Down

1. Eight less one is __.
2. You can __ addition to help you subtract.
3. In a subtraction problem, you know the __ and one part.

Word list:
- total
- ~~think~~
- ~~part~~
- ~~seven~~
- ~~nine~~
- ~~one~~
- ~~subtract~~

Crossword grid:
- 1 Across: s u b t r a c t
- Down 1: s e v e n
- Down 2: t h i n k
- 4 Across: o n e
- Down 3: t o t a l
- 5 Across: n i n e
- 6 Across: p a r t

© ORIGO Education

I. Circle the dominoes that show a **double-plus-I** fact.

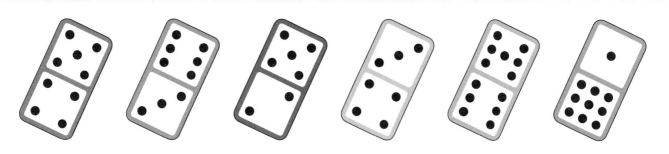

2. Write the missing number and draw the matching dots on each card. Then complete the addition facts.

a.

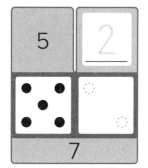

$5 + \boxed{} = 7$

b.

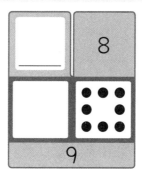

$\boxed{} + 8 = 9$

c.

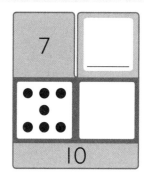

$7 + \boxed{} = 10$

Preparing for Module 7

Write the matching number of tens and ones on the expander. Then write the number name.

a.

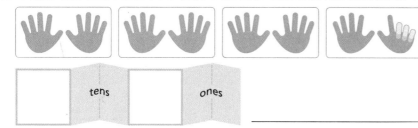

b.

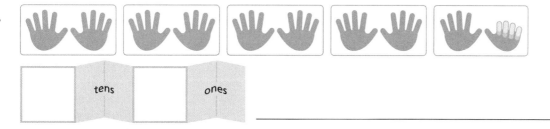

Step In

There are **9** pancakes in a stack. If **6** pancakes are eaten, how many pancakes will be left?

Complete each equation to show the number of pancakes that will be left.

Which equation would you use to solve this problem?

$9 - 6 = 3$

think

$6 + 3 = 9$

Complete each equation.

$8 - 2 = 6$ $10 - 9 = 1$ $6 - 1 = 5$ $5 - 3 = 2$

Circle the equations that you solved by thinking of addition.

How did you decide which equations to circle?

Step Up

1. Draw dots to figure out the missing part. Then complete the facts to match.

a. **6 dots in total**

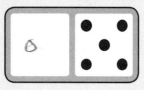

$6 - 5 = 1$

think

$5 + 1 = 6$

b. **7 dots in total**

$7 - 2 = 7$

think

$2 + 7 = 7$

2. Figure out the number of dots that are covered.
Then complete the facts.

a. 8 dots in total

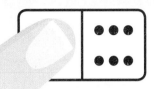

$8 - 6 = \boxed{2}$

$6 + \boxed{2} = 8$

b. 10 dots in total

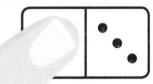

$10 - 3 = \boxed{7}$

$3 + \boxed{7} = 10$

c. 6 dots in total

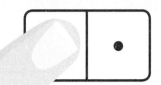

$6 - 1 = \boxed{5}$

$1 + \boxed{5} = 6$

d. 3 dots in total

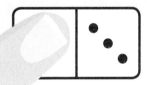

$3 - 3 = \boxed{0}$

$3 + \boxed{0} = 3$

e. 7 dots in total

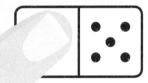

$7 - 5 = \boxed{2}$

$5 + \boxed{2} = 7$

f. 10 dots in total

$10 - 1 = \boxed{9}$

$1 + \boxed{9} = 10$

3. Write each answer.

a. $7 - 6 = \boxed{1}$

b. $4 - 2 = \boxed{2}$

c. $10 - 8 = \boxed{2}$

Step Ahead Solve this problem.
Show your thinking.

Hailey has 8 pennies. She gives
2 pennies to her sister, and 4 pennies
to her brother. How many pennies
does Hailey have left?

_____ pennies

Step In   There are 8 balls in a box. 4 balls are taken. How many balls are left?

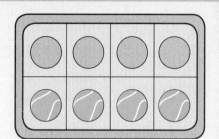

How could you figure out the answer without looking at the picture?

Complete this sentence.

see → 8 – 4 = 4

think → 4 + 4 = 8

What are some other doubles facts that you know?

Step Up   I. Write the doubles addition fact to match each total.

a.   6 + 6 = 12

b.   18 = 9 + 9

c.   4 + 4 = 8

d.   2 = 1 + 1

e.   5 + 5 = 10

f.   14 = 7 + 7

g.   2 + 2 = 4

h.   20 = 10 + 10

i.   8 + 8 = 16

j.   6 = 3 + 3

2. Figure out the number of dots that are covered.
Then complete the facts.

a. $12 - 6 =$ `6`

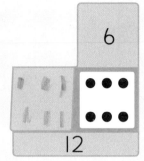

6

12

$6 + $ `6` $ = 12$

b. $4 - 2 =$ `2`

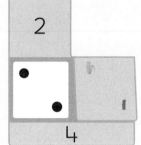

2

4

$2 + $ `2` $ = 4$

c. $16 - 8 =$ `8`

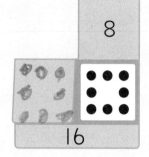

8

16

$8 + $ `8` $ = 16$

d. $2 - 1 =$ [ ]

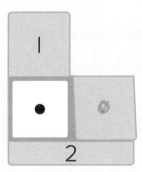

1

2

$1 + $ `1` $ = 2$

e. $14 - 7 =$ `7`

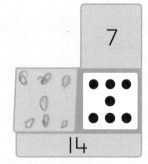

7

14

$7 + $ `7` $ = 14$

f. $18 - 9 =$ `9`

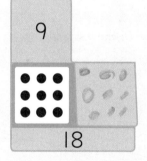

9

18

$9 + $ `8` $ = 18$

Step Ahead

Andre rolls a standard number cube two
times. He rolls the same number both times.
The total of the two rolls is 6. `6`

What number did he roll? ___

Computation Practice   **Where do superheroes go shopping?**

★   Complete the equations.

★   Write each letter above its matching total at the bottom of the page.

$15 + 1 = 16$ a

$1 + 7 = 8$ a

$17 + 2 = 19$ t

$9 + 2 = 11$ u

$9 + 1 = 10$ p

$4 + 3 = 7$ k

$13 + 2 = 15$ h

$19 + 1 = 20$ e

$1 + 17 = 18$ r

$2 + 10 = 12$ e

$4 + 2 = 6$ m

$2 + 12 = 14$ e

$15 + 2 = 17$ t

$3 + 6 = 9$ t

$2 + 3 = 5$ r

$2 + 11 = 13$ s

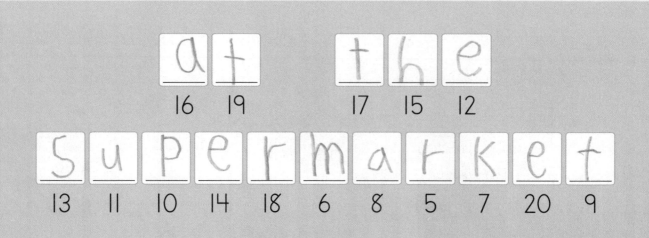

a   t   t   h   e
16 19   17 15 12

s   u   p   e   r   m   a   r   k   e   t
13 11 10 14 18 6   8   5   7   20 9

1. Circle the dominoes that show
a **double-plus-2** fact.

FROM 1.5.4

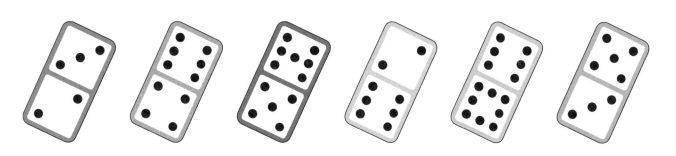

2. Figure out the number of dots that are covered.
Then complete the facts.

FROM 1.6.5

a. 9 dots in total	b. 8 dots in total	c. 7 dots in total

9 − 2 = ☐

2 + ☐ = 9

8 − 5 = ☐

5 + ☐ = 8

7 − 1 = ☐

1 + ☐ = 7

Preparing for Module 7

Write the number of tens and ones.
Then write the matching numeral.

a.

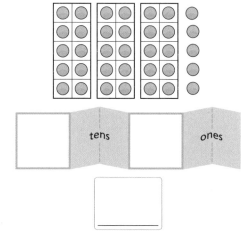

☐ tens ☐ ones

☐

b.

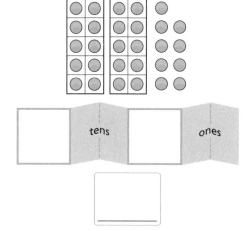

☐ tens ☐ ones

☐

Step In

Sara has 16 baseball cards. She gives some cards to a friend. Sara now has 8 cards.

How many cards did she give away?

Circle the thinking you could use to solve this problem.

$8 + 8 = 16$ $8 - 8 = 0$ $16 - 8 = 8$ $16 + 8 = 24$

When using addition to solve a subtraction problem the answer is the unknown part.

I can solve the above problem by thinking $8 + \_\_ = 16$. The answer is 8, not 16.

How could you use addition to solve this problem?

What addition fact could you write?

$12 - 6 = \boxed{6}$

Step Up

1. Draw dots to figure out the missing part. Then complete the facts to match.

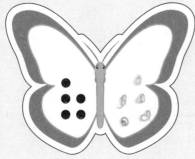

a. 10 dots in total

$10 - 5 = \boxed{5}$

$5 + \boxed{5} = 10$

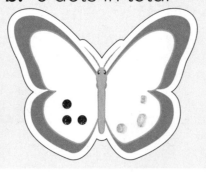

b. 6 dots in total

$6 - 3 = \boxed{3}$

$3 + \boxed{3} = 6$

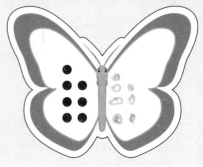

c. 14 dots in total

$14 - 7 = \boxed{7}$

$7 + \boxed{7} = 14$

2. Figure out the number of dots that are covered.
Then complete the facts.

a. 8 dots in total

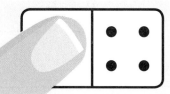

8 – 4 = 4

4 + 4 = 8

b. 4 dots in total

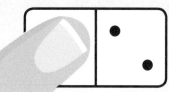

4 – 2 = 2

2 + 2 = 4

c. 18 dots in total

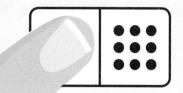

18 – 9 = 9

9 + 9 = 18

d. 16 dots in total

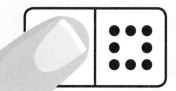

16 – 8 = 8

8 + 8 = 16

e. 12 dots in total

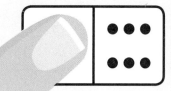

12 – 6 = 6

6 + 6 = 12

f. 6 dots in total

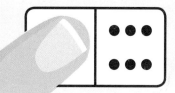

6 – 6 = 0

6 + 0 = 6

3. Write each answer.

a. 18 – 9 = 9

b. 20 – 10 = 10

c. 8 – 0 = 8

Step Ahead Samuel has 8 pennies. He gives 2 pennies to his sister and 2 pennies to his brother. How many pennies does he have left? Show your thinking.

4 pennies

Step In This strip of paper was folded and then opened out again. The dotted line shows where it was folded.

How could you prove that the strip of paper was folded in half?

Which of these strips was not folded in half? How do you know?

Step Up **I.** Color red one of the parts in each strip. Then circle the strips that show **one-half** in red.

a.

b.

c.

d.

e.

2. How did you decide which strips in Question I show one-half?

I circled the ones that are equal

3. Draw a line to split each strip in half.

a.
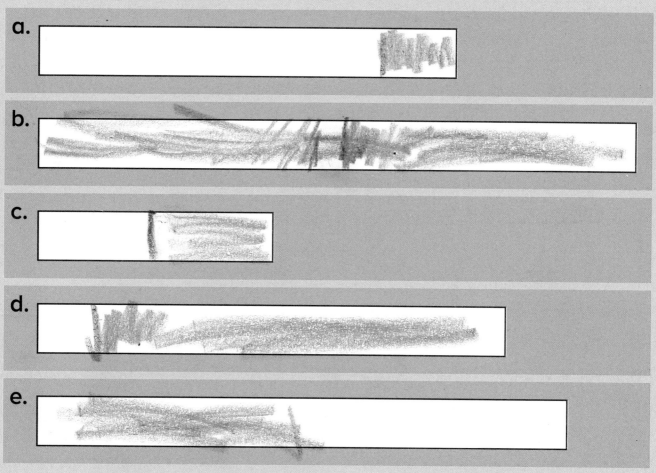

b.

c.

d.

e.

Step Ahead Color this strip to show a fraction that is a **little more** than one-half.

Think and Solve Read the clues. Use the letters to answer.

Clues

- **M** and **N** weigh the same.

- **O** is heavier than **M**.

- **P** is lighter than **N**.

a. Which is heaviest? ☐

b. Which is lightest? ☐

Words at Work a. Write about where you have seen **one-half**.

b. Draw a picture to show what you saw.

1. Color blocks to match each number name. Then write the numbers to complete the statement.

fourteen	forty-one

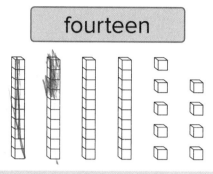 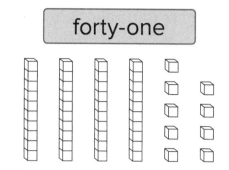

$\boxed{49}$ is less than $\boxed{}$

2. Figure out the number of dots that are covered. Then complete the facts.

a. 14 dots in total

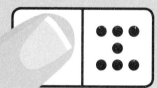

14 − 7 = $\boxed{21}$

7 + $\boxed{}$ = 14

b. 6 dots in total

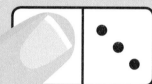

6 − 3 = $\boxed{3}$

3 + $\boxed{}$ = 6

c. 16 dots in total

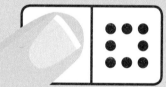

16 − 8 = $\boxed{}$

8 + $\boxed{}$ = 16

Preparing for Module 7 Write each time.

a.

$\boxed{}$ o'clock

b.

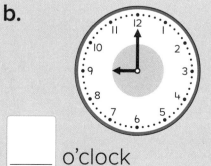

$\boxed{}$ o'clock

c.

$\boxed{}$ o'clock

Step In

This sheet of paper was folded and opened out again.

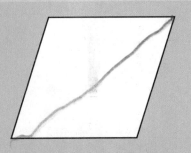

What do you notice?

What is another way you could fold the sheet in half?

How many different ways could you fold the sheet in half?

How could you prove that a sheet of paper has been folded in half?

Which of these has not been folded in half? How do you know?

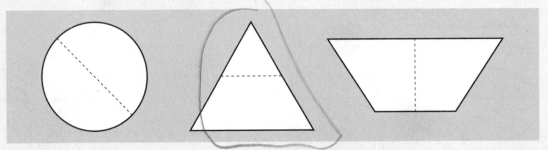

Step Up

1. Draw a line on each of these to show halves.

a.

b.

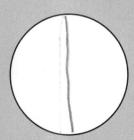

c.

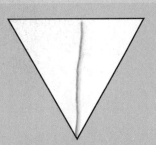

d.

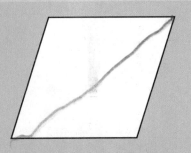

© ORIGO Education

2. Color red **one** of the parts in each of these.
Then circle each picture that shows **one-half** in red.

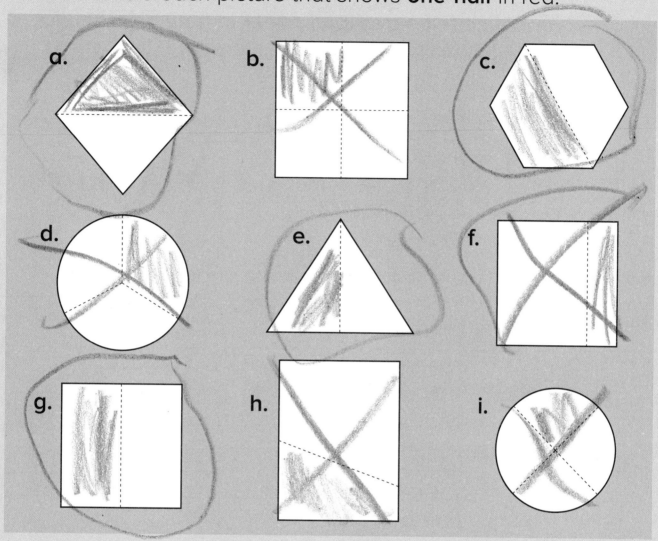

Step Ahead   Color parts to match each label.

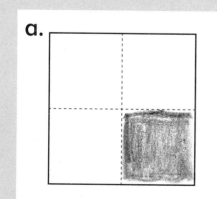

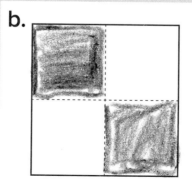

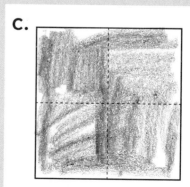

less than one-half

one-half

more than one-half

Common fractions: Identifying examples of one-fourth (length model)

Step In

Katherine folds a strip of paper in half. She then folds the same strip of paper in half again.

The strip of paper is now folded into **fourths**. Did you know that fourths are sometimes called **quarters**?

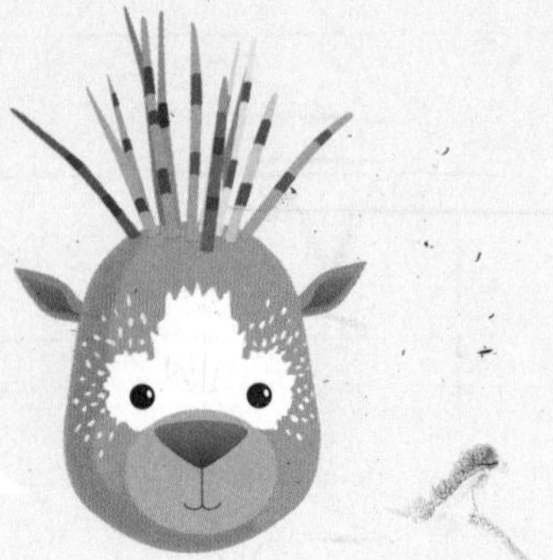

Draw lines on this strip where you think the paper was folded.

How did you decide where to draw the fold lines?

Which of these strips is not folded into fourths? How do you know?

Step Up

1. Draw lines on each strip to show fourths.

a.

b.

2. Color red **one** of the parts in each strip.
Then circle the strips that show **one-fourth** in red.

a.

b.

c.

d.

e.

3. Look at the strip in Question 2b.
How did you decide if one-fourth of this strip is red?

The Parts are not equal.

Step Ahead Color this strip to show a fraction that is a little less than one-fourth.

Computation Practice   **What do you give an elephant with big feet?**

★ Complete the equations.

★ Write each letter above its matching total at the bottom of the page.

7 + 2 = 9   r   9 + 2 = 11   o

5 + 5 = 10   o   2 + 4 = 6   s

2 + 1 = 3   l   3 + 1 = 4   o

1 + 4 = 5   t   4 + 3 = 7   o

3 + 5 = 8   f   6 + 6 = 12   m

l o t s _ o f _ r o o m

3   4   5   6   7   8   9   10   11   12

1. Write these numbers in order from **least** to **greatest**.

a.

| 12 | 18 | 22 | 15 |

12 15 19 ___

b.

| 38 | 41 | 83 | 75 |

___ ___ ___ ___

c.

| 32 | 39 | 41 | 40 |

___ ___ ___ ___

d.

| 25 | 29 | 31 | 21 |

___ ___ ___ ___

2. Draw a line on each of these to show **halves**.

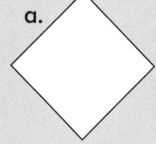 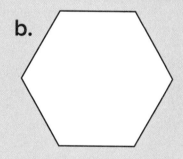 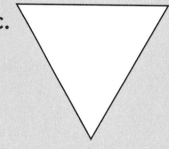

a.   b.   c.

Draw hands on each clock to show the time.

a.   4 o'clock

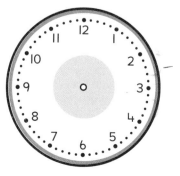

b.   11 o'clock

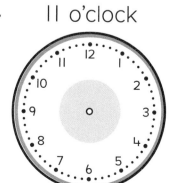

c.   7 o'clock

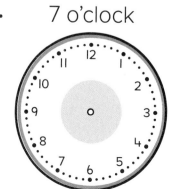

Step In   Look at this sheet of paper.

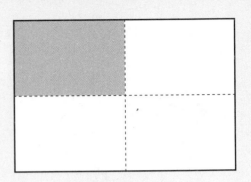

Describe the fraction that you see.

What is another name for one-fourth?

What other ways could you fold
the paper into fourths?

How can you prove that a sheet of paper has been folded
into fourths?

Which of these shows one-fourth? How do you know?

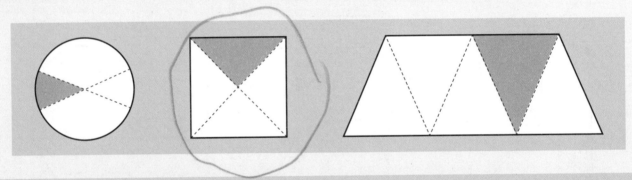

Step Up   1.   Draw one more line to show four parts the same
size. Then color **one-fourth**.

a.

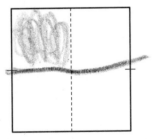

b.

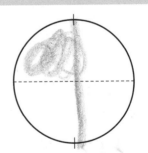

c.

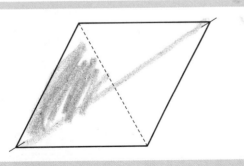

d.

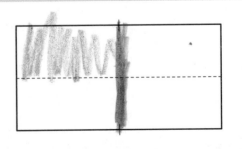

2. Color blue **one** of the parts in each.
Then circle each picture that shows **one-fourth** in blue.

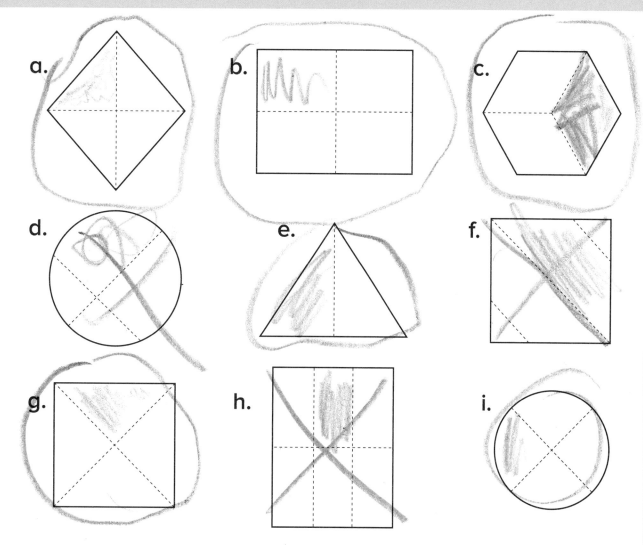

a.

b.

c.

d.

e.

f.

g.

h.

i.

Step Ahead

Do you think that one-fourth of this shape is shaded?
Explain your thinking in words.

If you draw
the lines you
can see one
four

Common fractions: Reinforcing one-half and one-fourth (area model)

Step In   Use red to show one-half of the same shape in three different ways.

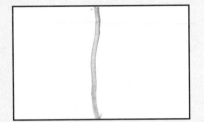 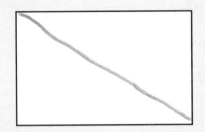 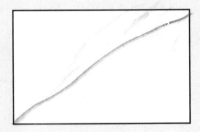

How could you prove that one-half of each shape is red?

Draw lines to show three different ways to split the same shape into fourths. Color one part of each shape blue.

 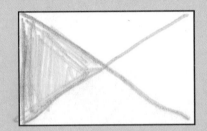 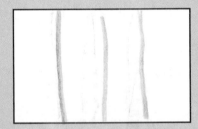

How could you prove that one-fourth of each shape is blue?
What are some other ways to color one-fourth?

Step Up   1.   Color one part of each shape red. Then circle the fraction name that describes the red part.

a.

one-half
or
one-fourth

b.
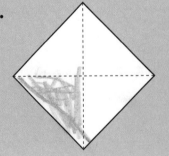

one-half
or
one-fourth

c.
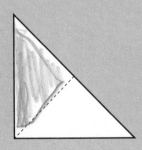

one-half
or
one-fourth

2. For each shape write the fraction that is shaded.
For some shapes neither one-half nor one-fourth is shaded.
For these shapes write **neither**.

a.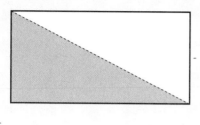

one - halh

b.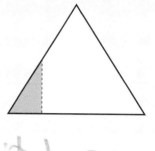

neither

c.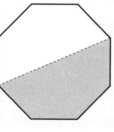

one - half

d.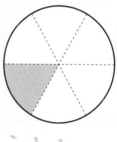

neither

e.

one - fourth

f.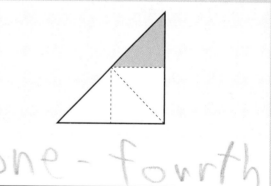

one - fourth

Step Ahead   Look at Question 2f. How did you decide what
fraction is shaded? Write your thinking in words.

They are the same

shape, Just rotated.

Think and Solve THINK TANK

a. Write the number of 🍎 in each column.

A = ☐   B = ☐   C = ☐

D = ☐   E = ☐

b. Rewrite the numbers in order from **greatest** to **least**.

☐ ☐ ☐ ☐ ☐

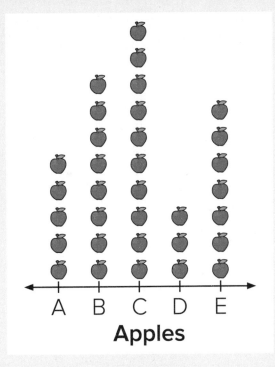

A B C D E

Apples

Words at Work

Write about how you could prove that a sheet of paper has been folded into fourths.
You can fold a sheet of paper to help.

Ongoing Practice

I. Draw ⌒ to connect the dots in order.

2nd

3rd •

9th
•

• 8th

1st

• 10th

4th •

• 7th

5th

6th

2. Draw one more line in each shape to show four parts the same size. Then color **one-fourth**.

a.

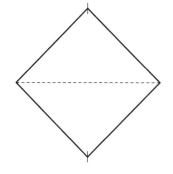

b.

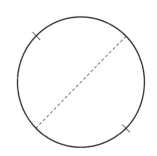

c.

Preparing for Module 7 Write each time on the digital clock.

a.

b.

c.

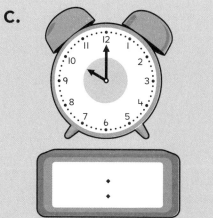

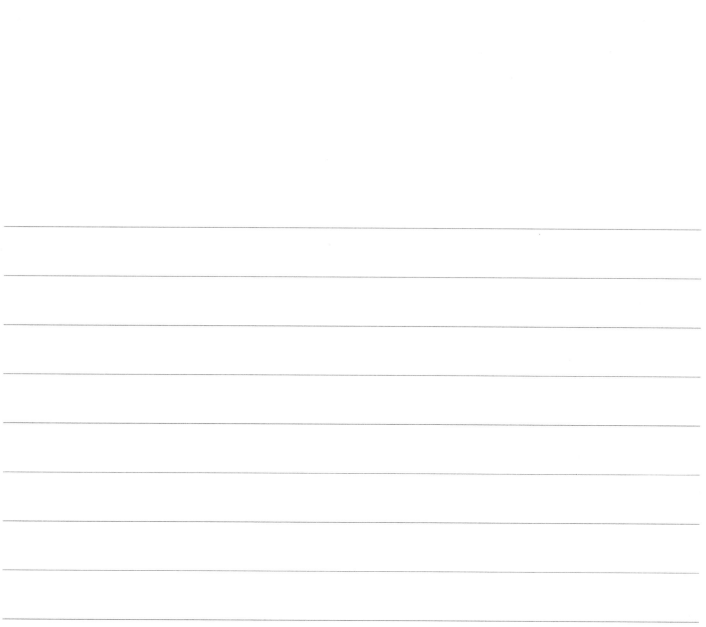

STUDENT GLOSSARY

2D shape

A **two-dimensional (2D) shape** has straight sides, curved edges, or straight sides and curved edges. For example:

 triangle

 circle

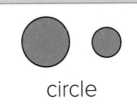 squares

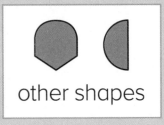 other shapes

3D object

A **three-dimensional (3D) object** has flat surfaces, curved surfaces, or flat and curved surfaces. For example:

 cube

 sphere

 cone

 cylinder

Addition

Addition is finding the total when two or more parts are known. When adding, another word for total is **sum**.

Part + Part = Total
2 + 3 = 5

Capacity

Capacity tells the amount a container can hold. For example, a cup **holds less** than a juice bottle.

Common fraction

Common fractions describe equal parts of one whole.

 one-half

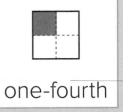 one-fourth

© ORIGO Education

STUDENT GLOSSARY

Comparing

When read from left to right, the symbol > means **is greater than**.
The symbol < means **is less than**.
For example: 2 < 6 means 2 **is less than** 6

Equals

2 and 3 **balances** 5
2 and 3 **is equal to** 5
2 + 3 = 5

Equation

An **equation** is a number sentence that uses the equals symbol.
For example: 7 + 8 = 15

Fact family

A **fact family** includes an addition fact,
its turnaround fact, and the two related
subtraction facts. For example:

4 + 2 = 6
2 + 4 = 6
6 − 4 = 2
6 − 2 = 4

Mass

Mass tells the amount something weighs.
For example, a cat **weighs more** than a mouse.

Mental computation strategies for addition

These are strategies you can use to figure out a mathematical
problem in your head.

Count-on	*See* 2 + 8	*think* 8 + 1 + 1
	See 58 + 24	*think* 58 + 10 + 10 + 4
Doubles	*See* 7 + 7	*think* double 7
	See 25 + 26	*think* double 25 plus 1 more
	See 35 + 37	*think* double 35 plus 2 more
Make-ten	*See* 9 + 4	*think* 9 + 1 + 3
	See 38 + 14	*think* 38 + 2 + 12
Place-value	*See* 32 + 27	*think* 32 + 20 + 7

Mental computation strategies for subtraction

These are strategies you can use to figure out a mathematical problem in your head.

Count-back   *See* 9 – 2   *think* 9 – 1 – 1
                       See 26 – 20 *think* 26 – 10 – 10

Think-addition   *See* 17 – 9   *think* 9 + 8 = 17 so 17 – 9 = 8

Number

Number tells "how many." For example, there are nine blocks in this group.

Number facts

Addition facts are all the addition equations that show two one-digit numbers being added. Addition facts can be written with the total at the start or at the end.

For example: 2 + 3 = 5 or 3 = 1 + 2

Subtraction facts are all the subtraction equations that are related to the addition facts.

For example: 5 – 2 = 3 or 3 – 2 = 1

Numeral

A **numeral** is the symbol for a number.

Related subtraction facts

Each subtraction fact has a **related** fact.

For example: 7 – 4 = 3 and 7 – 3 = 4

Subtraction

Subtraction is finding a part when the total and one part are known.

$$\text{Total} - \text{Part} = \text{Part}$$
$$5 \;-\; 2 \;=\; 3$$
$$\text{Part} + \underline{} = \text{Total}$$
$$2 \;+\; \underline{} \;=\; 5$$

Tally

A **tally** is a single mark used to record the number of times something occurs. A gate tally is a mark used to group every five tallies. For example:

||||
four tally marks

Turnaround fact

Each addition fact has a related **turnaround fact**.

For example: $2 + 3 = 5$ and $3 + 2 = 5$

TEACHER INDEX

TEACHER INDEX